Project-Based Inquiry Science™

DIVING INTO SCIENCE

PBIS™
Launcher Unit

IT's ABOUT TIME®

HERFF JONES EDUCATION DIVISION

IT's ABOUT TIME®

HERFF JONES EDUCATION DIVISION

84 Business Park Drive, Armonk, NY 10504
Phone (914) 273-2233 Fax (914) 273-2227
www.its-about-time.com

President
Tom Laster

Director of Product Development
Barbara Zahm, Ph.D.

Creative Director, Design
John Nordland

Project Development Editor
Ruta Demery

Editorial Coordinator
Lakiska Flippin

Editor
Sarah V. Gruber

Assistant Editor
Rhonda Gordon

Production/Studio Manager
Robert Schwalb

Layout and Production
Kadi Sarv
Erich Reichert

Creative Artwork
Dennis Falcon

Technical Art
Marie Killoran

Photo Research
Carlo Cantavero

Content and Safety Reviewer
Edward Robeck

ISBN-13: 978-1-58591-600-9

1 2 3 4 5 VH 11 10 09 08

This project was supported, in part, by the **National Science Foundation**
under grant nos. 0137807, 0527341, 0639978.
Opinions expressed are those of the authors and not necessarily
those of the National Science Foundation.

PBIS Principal Investigators

Janet L. Kolodner is a Regents' Professor in the School of Interactive Computing in Georgia Institute of Technology's College of Computing. Since 1978, her research has focused on learning from experience, both in computers and in people. She pioneered the Artificial Intelligence method called *case-based reasoning*, providing a way for computers to solve new problems based on their past experiences. Her book, *Case-Based Reasoning*, synthesizes work across the case-based reasoning research community from its inception to 1993.

Since 1994, Dr. Kolodner has focused on the applications and implications of case-based reasoning for education. In her approach to science education, called Learning by Design™ (LBD), students learn science while pursuing design challenges. Dr. Kolodner has investigated how to create a culture of collaboration and rigorous science talk in classrooms, how to use a project challenge to promote focus on science content, and how students learn and develop when classrooms function as learning communities. Currently, Dr. Kolodner is investigating how to help young people come to think of themselves as scientific reasoners. Dr. Kolodner's research results have been widely published, including in *Cognitive Science, Design Studies,* and *The Journal of the Learning Sciences.*

Dr. Kolodner was founding Director of Georgia Techs' EduTech Institute, served as coordinator of Georgia Techs' Cognitive Science program for many years, and is founding Editor in Chief of *The Journal of the Learning Sciences.* She is a founder of the International Society for the Learning Sciences (ISLS), and she served as its first Executive Officer. She is a fellow of the American Association of Artificial Intelligence (AAAI).

Joseph S. Krajcik is a Professor of Science Education and Associate Dean for Research in the School of Education at the University of Michigan. He works with teachers in science classrooms to bring about sustained change by creating classroom environments in which students find solutions to important intellectual questions that subsume essential curriculum standards and use learning technologies as productivity tools. He seeks to discover what students learn in such environments, as well as to explore and find solutions to challenges that teachers face in enacting such complex instruction. Professor Krajcik has authored and co-authored over 100 manuscripts and makes frequent presentations at international, national and regional conferences that focus on his research, as well as presentations that translate research findings into classroom practice. He is a fellow of the American Association for the Advancement of Science and served as president of the National Association for Research in Science Teaching. Dr. Krajcik co-directs the Center for Highly Interactive Classrooms, Curriculum and Computing in Education at the University of Michigan and is a co-principal investigator in the Center for Curriculum Materials in Science and The National Center for Learning and Teaching Nanoscale Science and Engineering. In 2002, Professor Krajcik was honored to receive a Guest Professorship from Beijing Normal University in Beijing, China. In winter 2005, he was the Weston Visiting Professor of Science Education at the Weizmann Institute of Science in Rehovot, Israel.

Daniel C. Edelson is director of the Geographic Data in Education (GEODE) Initiative at Northwestern University where he is an Associate Professor of the Learning Sciences and Computer Science. Trained as a computer and cognitive scientist, Dr. Edelson develops and studies software and curricula that are informed by contemporary research on learning and motivation. Since 1992, Dr. Edelson has directed a series of projects exploring the use of technology as a catalyst for reform in science education and has led the development of a number of software environments for education. These include My World GIS, a geographic information system for inquiry-based learning, and WorldWatcher, a data visualization and analysis system for gridded geographic data, both of which have been recognized by educators for their contributions to Earth science education. Dr. Edelson is the author of the high school environmental science text, *Investigations in Environmental Science: A Case-Based Approach to the Study of Environmental Systems*. Dr. Edelson is currently engaged in research on professional development and implementation support for schools that have adopted *Investigations in Environmental Science*.

Since 1995, he has been the principal investigator on more than a dozen NSF-funded educational research and development grants, and he is a member of the leadership team of the NSF-funded Center for Curriculum Materials in Science. His research has been widely published, including in the *Journal of the Learning Sciences, The Journal of Research on Science Teaching, The Journal of Geoscience Education*, and *Science Teacher*.

Brian J. Reiser is a Professor of Learning Sciences in the School of Education and Social Policy at Northwestern University. Professor Reiser served as chair of Northwestern's Learning Sciences Ph.D. program from 1993, shortly after its inception, until 2001. His research focuses on the design and enactment of learning environments that support students' inquiry in science, including both science curriculum materials and scaffolded software tools. His research investigates the design of learning environments that scaffold scientific practices, including investigation, argumentation, and explanation; design principles for technology-infused curricula that engage students in inquiry projects; and the teaching practices that support student inquiry.

Professor Reiser also directed BGuILE (Biology Guided Inquiry Learning Environments) to develop software tools for supporting middle school and high school students in analyzing data and constructing explanations with biological data. Reiser is a co-principal investigator in the NSF Center for Curriculum Materials in Science. He recently served as a member of the NRC panel authoring the report *Taking Science to School*. Professor Reiser received his Ph.D. in Cognitive Science from Yale University in 1983.

Acknowledgements

Three research teams contributed to the development of Project-Based Inquiry Science (PBIS): a team at Georgia Institute of Technology headed by Janet L. Kolodner, a team at Northwestern University headed by Daniel Edelson and Brian Reiser, and a team at University of Michigan headed by Joseph Krajcik and Ron Marx. Each of the PBIS units was originally developed by one of these teams and then later revised and edited to be a part of the full three-year middle-school curriculum that became PBIS.

PBIS has its roots in two educational approaches, Project-Based Science and Learning by Design™. Project-Based Science suggests that students should learn science through engaging in the same kinds of inquiry practices scientists use, in the context of scientific problems relevant to their lives and using tools authentic to science. Project-Based Science was originally conceived in the hi-ce Center at University of Michigan, with funding from the National Science Foundation. Learning by Design™ derives from Problem-Based Learning and suggests sequencing, social practices, and reflective activities for promoting learning. It engages students in design practices, including the use of iteration and deliberate reflection. LBD was conceived at Georgia Institute of Technology, with funding from the National Science Foundation, DARPA, and the McDonnell Foundation.

The development of the integrated PBIS curriculum was supported by the National Science Foundation under grants no. 0137807, 0527341, and 0639978. Any opinions, findings and conclusions, or recommendations expressed in this material are those of the authors and do not necessarily reflect the views of the National Science Foundation.

PBIS Team

Principal Investigator
Janet L. Kolodner

Co-Principal Investigators
Daniel C. Edelson
Joseph S. Krajcik
Brian J. Reiser

NSF Program Officer
Gerhard Salinger

Curriculum Developers
Michael T. Ryan
Mary L. Starr

Teacher's Edition Developers
Rebecca M. Schneider
Mary L. Starr

Literacy Specialist
LeeAnn M. Sutherland

NSF Program Reviewer
Arthur Eisenkraft

Project Coordinator
Juliana Lancaster

External Evaluators
The Learning Partnership
Steven M. McGee
Jennifer Witers

The Georgia Institute of Technology Team

Project Director:
Janet L. Kolodner

Development of PBIS units at the Georgia Institute of Technology was conducted in conjunction with the Learning by Design™ Research group (LBD), Janet L. Kolodner, PI.

Lead Developers, Physical Science:
David Crismond
Michael T. Ryan

Lead Developer, Earth Science:
Paul J. Camp

Assessment and Evaluation:
Barbara Fasse
Daniel Hickey
Jackie Gray
Laura Vandewiele
Jennifer Holbrook

Project Pioneers:
JoAnne Collins
David Crismond
Joanna Fox
Alice Gertzman
Mark Guzdial
Cindy Hmelo-Silver
Douglas Holton
Roland Hubscher
N. Hari Narayanan
Wendy Newstetter
Valery Petrushin
Kathy Politis
Sadhana Puntambekar
David Rector
Janice Young

The Northwestern University Team

Project Directors:
Daniel Edelson
Brian Reiser

Lead Developer, Biology:
David Kanter

Lead Developers, Earth Science:
Jennifer Mundt Leimberer
Darlene Slusher

Development of PBIS units at Northwestern was conducted in conjunction with:

The Center for Learning Technologies in Urban Schools (LeTUS) at Northwestern, and the Chicago Public Schools
Louis Gomez, PI;
Clifton Burgess, PI
for Chicago Public Schools.

The BioQ Collaborative
David Kanter, PI.

The Biology Guided Learning Environments (BGuILE) Project
Brian Reiser, PI.

The Geographic Data in Education (GEODE) Initiative
Daniel Edelson, Director

The Center for Curriculum Materials in Science at Northwestern
Brian Reiser,
Daniel Edelson,
Bruce Sherin, PIs.

The University of Michigan Team

Project Directors:
Joseph Krajcik
Ron Marx

Literacy Specialist:
LeeAnn M. Sutherland

Project Coordinator:
Mary L. Starr

Development of PBIS units at University of Michigan was conducted in conjunction with:

The Center for Learning Technologies in Urban Schools (LeTUS)
Ron Marx, Phyllis Blumenfeld,
Barry Fishman,
Joseph Krajcik,
Elliot Soloway, PIs.

The Detroit Public Schools
Juanita Clay-Chambers
Deborah Peek-Brown

The Center for Highly Interactive Computing in Education (hi-ce)
Ron Marx,
Phyllis Blumenfeld,
Barry Fishman,
Joe Krajcik,
Elliot Soloway,
Elizabeth Moje,
LeeAnn Sutherland, PIs.

Project-Based Inquiry Science

Field-Test Teachers

National Field Test
Tamica Andrew
Leslie Baker
Jeanne Bayer
Gretchen Bryant
Boris Consuegra
Daun D'Aversa
Candi DiMauro
Kristie L. Divinski
Donna M. Dowd
Jason Fiorito
Lara Fish
Christine Gleason
Christine Hallerman
Terri L. Hart-Parker
Jennifer Hunn
Rhonda K. Hunter
Jessica Jones
Dawn Kuppersmith
Anthony F. Lawrence
Ann Novak
Rise Orsini
Tracy E. Parham
Cheryl Sgro-Ellis
Debra Tenenbaum
Sara B. Topper
Becky Watts
Debra A. Williams
Ingrid M. Woolfolk
Ping-Jade Yang

New York City Field Test
Several sequences of PBIS units have been field tested in New York City under the leadership of Whitney Lukens, Staff Developer for Region 9, and Greg Borman, Science Instructional Specialist, New York City Department of Education

6th Grade
Norman Agard
Tazinmudin Ali
Heather Guthartz
Aniba
Asher Arzonane
Asli Aydin

Joshua Blum
Filomena Borrero
Shareese Blakely
John J. Blaylock
Tsedey Bogale
Zachary Brachio
Thelma Brown
Alicia Browne-Jones
Scott Bullis
Maximo Cabral
Lionel Callender
Matthew Carpenter
Ana Maria Castro
Diane Castro
Anne Chan
Ligia Chiorean
Boris Consuegra
Careen Halton Cooper
Cinnamon Czarnecki
Kristin Decker
Nancy Dejean
Gina DiCicco
Donna Dowd
Lizanne Espina
Joan Ferrato
Matt Finnerty
Jacqueline Flicker
Helen Fludd
Leigh Summers Frey
Helene Friedman-Hager
Diana Gering
Matthew Giles
Lucy Gill
Steven Gladden
Greg Grambo
Carrie Grodin-Vehling
Stephan Joanides
Kathryn Kadei
Paraskevi Karangunis
Cynthia Kerns
Martine Lalanne
Erin Lalor
Jennifer Lerman
Sara Lugert
Whitney Lukens
Dana Martorella
Christine Mazurek
Janine McGeown
Chevelle McKeever
Kevin Meyer
Jennifer Miller

Nicholas Miller
Diana Neligan
Caitlin Van Ness
Marlyn Orque
Eloisa Gelo Ortiz
Gina Papadopoulos
Tim Perez
Albertha Petrochilos
Christopher Poli
Kristina Rodriguez
Nadiesta Sanchez
Annette Schavez
Hilary Sedgwitch
Elissa Seto
Laura Shectman
Audrey Shmuel
Ragini Singhal
Katherine Silva
C. Nicole Smith
Gitangali Sohit
Justin Stein
Thomas Tapia
Eilish Walsh-Lennon
Lisa Wong
Brian Yanek
Cesar Yarleque
David Zaretsky
Colleen Zarinsky

7th Grade
Mayra Amaro
Emmanuel Anastasiou
Cheryl Barnhill
Bryce Cahn
Ligia Chiorean
Ben Colella
Boris Consuegra
Careen Halton Cooper
Elizabeth Derse
Urmilla Dhanraj
Gina DiCicco
Lydia Doubleday
Lizanne Espina
Matt Finnerty
Steven Gladden
Stephanie Goldberg
Nicholas Graham
Robert Hunter
Charlene Joseph
Ketlynne Joseph
Kimberly Kavazanjian

Christine Kennedy
Bakwah Kotung
Lisa Kraker
Anthony Lett
Herb Lippe
Jennifer Lopez
Jill Mastromarino
Kerry McKie
Christie Morgado
Patrick O'Connor
Agnes Ochiagha
Tim Perez
Nadia Piltser
Chris Poli
Carmelo Ruiz
Kim Sanders
Leslie Schiavone
Ileana Solla
Jacqueline Taylor
Purvi Vora
Ester Wiltz
Carla Yuille
Marcy Sexauer Zacchea
Lidan Zhou

DIVING INTO SCIENCE

Diving Into Science

Diving Into Science was developed at the Georgia Institute of Technology as part of the Learning by Design™ initiative and was originally titled *Apollo 13: The Launcher Unit*.

Apollo 13

Major Authors

Michael T. Ryan

Janet L. Kolodner

Jennifer Holbrook

David Crismond

Contributing Authors

Paul J. Camp

Jackie Gray

Jennifer Turns

Formative Development

David Crismond

Joanna Fox

Jackie Gray

Cami Heck

Jennifer Holbrook

Susan McClendon

Kristine Nagel

Lindy Wine

Janice Young

Pilot Teachers

Barbara Blasch

Audrey Daniel

Pam Davis

Carmen Dillard

Yvette Fernandez

Joyce Gamble

Dorothy Hicks

Daphne Islam-Gordon

Rudo Kashiri

Marni Klein

Toni Laman

Paige Lefont

Susan McClendon

Carol Pennington

Cindy Rhew

Mike Ryan

Maureen Shalinski

Jeffrey Slater

Delilah Springer

Lindy Wine

Avis Winfield

Mary Winn

Diving Into Science

PBIS Development Team

Michael T. Ryan

Mary L. Starr

Janet L. Kolodner

Contributing Field-test teachers

Asher Arzonane

Suzy Bachman

Greg Borman

Matthew Carpenter

Anne Chan

Lizanne Espina

Enrique Garcia

Steven Gladden

Greg Grambo

Lillian Arlia Grippo

Dani Horowitz

Nicole Shiu Horowitz

Stephan Joanides

Verneda Johnson

Sunny Kam

Crystal Marsh

Kristin McNichol

Melissa Nathan

Tim Perez

Christopher Poli

Nadiesta Sanchez

Caitlin Van Ness

Melanie Wenger

Cesar Yarleque

Renee Zalewitz

Development of *Diving Into Science*, previously called *Apollo 13: The Launcher Unit*, was supported in part by the National Science Foundation under grants no. 9553583, 9818828, and 0208059 and by grants from the McDonnell Foundation, the BellSouth Foundation, the Woodruff Foundation, and the Georgia Tech Foundation. Any opinions, findings, and conclusions or recommendations expressed in this material are those of the authors and do not necessarily reflect the views of the National Science Foundation.

Diving Into Science Table of Contents

Learning Set 1

The Book-Support Challenge 4

Collaboration, building on the work of others, iteration, criteria and constraints, design process, keeping good records, science of support.

1.1 Understand the Challenge
Identify Criteria and Constraints 5

1.2 Design
A Better Book-Support Design 7

1.3 Read
The Science of Structures 15

1.4 Design
Another Book-Support Challenge 20

Back to the Big Challenge 23

Learning Set 2

The Sandwich-Cookie Challenge 25

Recording information, graphing results, factors that lead to variation, reliability, inexactness and uncertainty in science.

2.1 Understand the Challenge
Identify Criteria and Constraints 26

2.2 Investigate
How Many Drops of Water Fit on a Penny? .. 27

2.3 Redesign Your Investigation
Getting to a Better Procedure 29

2.4 Investigate
How Many Drops of Water Fit on a Penny? .. 32

Back to the Big Challenge 34

Learning Set 3

The Whirligig Challenge 35

Factors that lead to variation, manipulated (independent) and responding (dependent) variables, designing experiments, reliability, fair tests, physics of falling objects, using evidence to support claims, explanation, collaboration.

3.1 Understand the Challenge
Thinking about How Things Fall 36

3.2 Plan
Whirligig Experiment 43

3.3 Investigate
Experiment with a Whirligig 47

3.4 Read
Whirligig Science 53

3.5 Explain
Create an Explanation 57

3.6 Iterate
More Science and More Explanation 63

3.7 What Have We Learned?
Back to the Whirligig Challenge 66

Learning Set 4

The Parachute Challenge 69

Fair tests, independent and dependent variables, designing experiments, keeping good records, graphing, physics of falling objects, using evidence to support claims, explanation, collaboration, iteration, applying science knowledge.

4.1 Understand the Challenge
Thinking about the Parachute Challenge 71

4.2 Investigate
Investigate Parachutes 76

4.3 Explain and Recommend
Explanations and Recommendations
about Parachutes 81

4.4 Read
Parachute Science 83

4.5 Plan
Design a Slow-Falling Parachute 90

4.6 Build and Test
Build and Test Your Parachute 94

4.7 Address the Challenge
Advise the Cereal Company 99

**How Do Scientists Work
Together to Solve Problems?** 100

Welcome to Project-Based Inquiry Science!

Dear Students,

This year, you will be learning the way scientists learn. You will explore interesting questions and challenges. You will learn new things. You will also learn exciting, new ways to think about the world around you.

Scientists learn as they are trying to answer a big question or solve a big challenge. To help them work on these big questions or challenges, scientists break them into smaller ones. For each smaller question or challenge, they read what other scientists already know, and they investigate, explore, gather evidence, and form explanations. This way, scientists build new knowledge as they answer these smaller questions. Then they use what they have learned to try to answer the big question or solve the big challenge. Along the way, scientists share what they have learned with other scientists. These other scientists can then use this new knowledge to address other questions and challenges.

Like scientists, you will be trying to answer big questions and solve big challenges this year. You will break these into smaller questions or challenges. For each smaller question or challenge, you'll read, investigate, explore, gather evidence, and form explanations. As you do these things, you will share what you are learning and work closely with your classmates. You and your classmates will help each other learn and successfully answer each unit's question or solve its challenge. At the end of each unit, you'll answer the big question or address the big challenge based on what you've learned. And you will have learned a lot!

PBIS was designed to support you as you become a student scientist. In fact, PBIS units were written by scientists who study how people learn and who want to help you become the best scientist you can be. We used what we know about learning to design ways to help you answer big questions and solve big challenges. What you learn this year about science will help you learn science in the future. The way you learn to think about questions and challenges will help you learn other subjects, too.

Each year begins with a launcher unit. Launcher units help your class learn to work together, help you become familiar with the ways scientists think and have discussions, and introduce you to the activities and tools you'll use throughout PBIS.

Have fun being a student scientist!

Janet L. Kolodner

Janet Kolodner (for the whole PBIS team)

Introducing PBIS

What Do Scientists Do?

1) Scientists...address big challenges and big questions.

You will find many different kinds of big challenges and questions in PBIS units. Some ask you to think about why something is a certain way. Some ask you to think about what causes something to change. Some challenge you to design a solution to a problem. Most of them are about things that can and do happen in the real world.

Understand the Big Challenge or Question

As you get started with each unit, you will do activities that help you understand the big question or challenge for that unit. You will think about what you already know that might help you, and you will identify some of the new things you will need to learn.

Project Board

The *Project Board* helps you keep track of your learning. For each challenge or question, you will use a *Project Board* to keep track of what you know, what you need to learn, and what you are learning. As you learn and gather evidence, you will record that on the *Project Board*. After you have answered each small question or challenge, you will return to the *Project Board* to record how what you've learned helps you answer the big question or challenge.

Learning Sets

Each unit is composed of a group of *Learning Sets*, one for each of the smaller questions that needs to be answered to address the big question or challenge. In each *Learning Set*, you will investigate and read to find answers to the *Learning Set's* question. You will also have a chance to share the results of your investigations with your classmates and work together to make sense of what you are learning. As you come to understand answers to the questions on the *Project Board*, you will record those answers and the evidence you've collected that convinces you of what you've learned. At the end of each *Learning Set*, you will apply what you've learned to the big question or challenge.

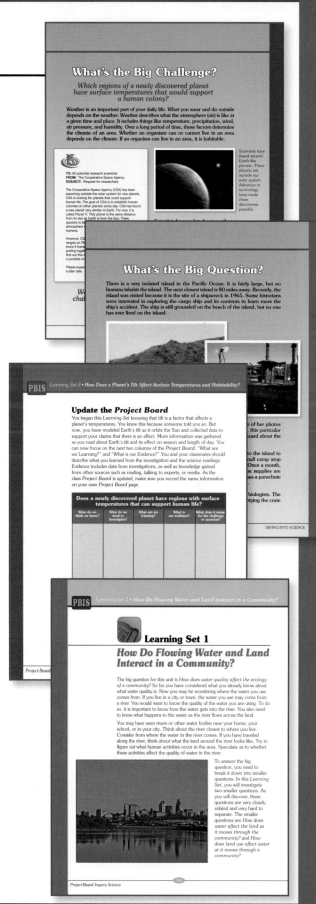

DIVING INTO SCIENCE

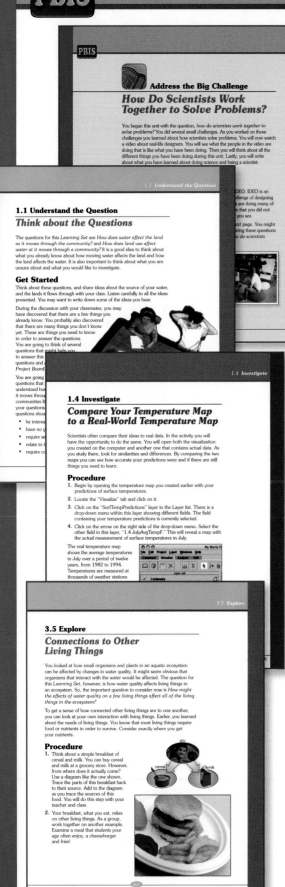

Address the Big Challenge/ Answer the Big Question

At the end of each unit, you will put everything you have learned together to tackle the big challenge or question.

2) Scientists...address smaller questions and challenges.

What You Do in a *Learning Set*

Understanding the Question or Challenge

At the start of each *Learning Set*, you will usually do activities that will help you understand the *Learning Set's* question or challenge and recognize what you already know that can help you answer the question or achieve the challenge. Usually, you'll visit the *Project Board* after these activities and record on it the even smaller questions that you need to investigate to answer a *Learning Set's* question.

Investigate/Explore

There are many different kinds of investigations you might do to find answers to questions. In the *Learning Sets* you might

- design and run experiments
- design and run simulations
- design and build models
- examine large sets of data

Don't worry if you haven't done these things before. The text will provide you with lots of help in designing your investigations and in analyzing your data.

Read

Like scientists, you will also read about the science you are learning. You'll read a little bit before you investigate, but most of the reading you do will be to help you understand what you've experienced or seen in an investigation. Each time you read, the text will include *Stop and Think* questions after the reading. These questions will help you gauge how well you understand what you have read. Usually, the class will discuss the answers to *Stop and Think* questions before going on so that everybody has a chance to make sense of the reading.

Design and Build

When the big challenge for a unit asks you to design something, the challenge in a *Learning Set* might also ask you to design something and make it work. Often you will design a part of the thing you will design and build for the big challenge. When a Learning Set challenges you to design and build something, you will do several things:

- identify what questions you need to answer to be successful
- investigate to find answers to those questions
- use those answers to plan a good design solution
- build and test your design

Because designs don't always work the way you want them to, you will usually do a design challenge more than once. Each time through, you will test your design. If your design doesn't work as well as you'd like, you will determine why it is not working and identify other things you need to learn to make it work better. Then you will learn those things and try again.

Explain and Recommend

A big part of what scientists do is explain, or try to make sense of why things happen the way they do. An explanation describes why something is the way it is or behaves the way it does. An explanation is a statement you make built from claims (what you think you know), evidence (from an investigation) that supports the claim, and science knowledge. As they learn, scientists get better at explaining. You'll see that you get better too as you work through the *Learning Sets*.

A recommendation is a special kind of claim—one where you advise somebody about what to do. You will make recommendations and support them with evidence, science knowledge, and explanations.

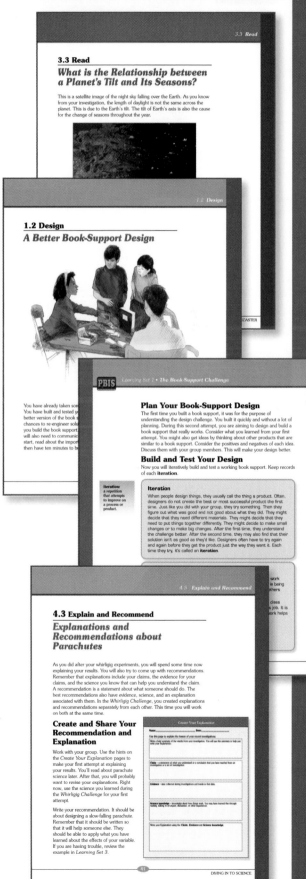

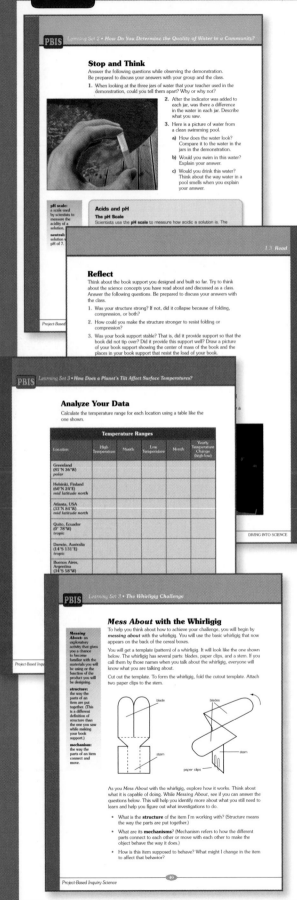

3) Scientists...reflect in many different ways.

PBIS provides guidance to help you think about what you are doing and to recognize what you are learning. Doing this often as you are working will help you be a successful student scientist.

Tools for Making Sense

Stop and Think

Stop and Think sections help you make sense of what you've been doing in the section you are working on. *Stop and Think* sections include a set of questions to help you understand what you've just read or done. Sometimes the questions will remind you of something you need to pay more attention to. Sometimes they will help you connect what you've just read to things you already know. When there is a *Stop and Think* in the text, you will work individually or with a partner to answer the questions, and then the whole class will discuss what you've learned.

Reflect

Reflect sections help you connect what you've just done with other things you've read or done earlier in the unit (or in another unit). When there is a *Reflect* in the text, you will work individually or with a partner or your small group to answer the questions, and then the whole class will discuss what you've learned. You may be asked to answer *Reflect* questions for homework.

Analyze Your Data

Whenever you have to analyze data, the text will provide hints about how to do that and what to look for.

Mess About

"Messing about" is a term that comes from design. It means exploring the materials you will be using for designing or building something or examining something that works like what you will be designing. Messing about helps you discover new ideas—and it can be a lot of fun. The text will usually give you ideas about things to notice as you are messing about.

What's the Point?

At the end of each *Learning Set*, you will find a summary, called *What's the Point*, of the important things we hope you learned from the *Learning Set*. These summaries can help you remember how what you did and learned is connected to the big challenge or question you are working on.

4) Scientists...collaborate.

Scientists never do all their work alone. They work with other scientists (collaborate) and share their knowledge. PBIS helps you be a student scientist by giving you lots of opportunities for sharing your findings, ideas, and discoveries with others (the way scientists do). You will work together in small groups to investigate, design, explain, and do other things. Sometimes you will work in pairs to figure things out together. You will also have lots of opportunities to share your findings with the rest of your classmates and make sense together of what you are learning.

Investigation Expo

In an *Investigation Expo*, small groups report to the class about an investigation they've done. For each *Investigation Expo*, you will make a poster detailing what you were trying to learn from your investigation, what you did, your data, and your interpretation of your data. The text gives you hints about what to present and what to look for in other groups' presentations. *Investigation Expos* are always followed by discussions about what you've learned and about how to do science well. You may also be asked to write a lab report following an investigation.

Plan Briefing/Solution Briefing/ Idea Briefing

Briefings are presentations of work in progress. They give you a chance to get advice from your classmates that can help you move forward. During a *Plan Briefing*, you present your plan to the class. It might be a plan for an experiment or a plan for solving a problem or achieving a challenge. During a *Solution Briefing*, you present your solution in progress and ask the class to help you make your solution better. During an *Idea Briefing*, you present your ideas. You get the best advice from your classmates when you present evidence in support of your plan, solution, or idea. Often, you will prepare a poster to help you make your presentation. Briefings are almost always followed by discussions of what you've learned and how you will move forward.

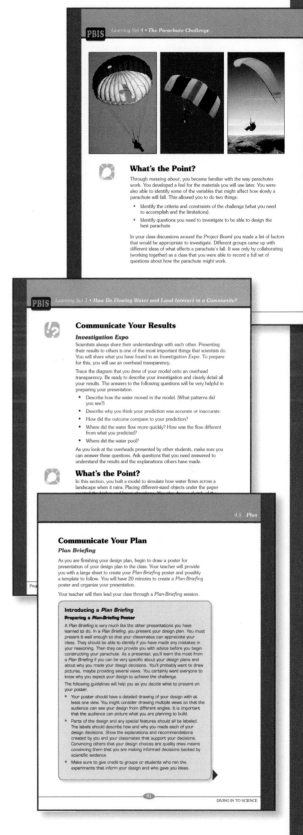

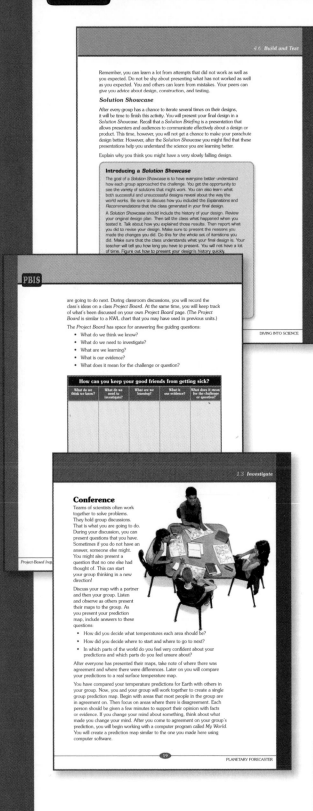

Solution Showcase

Solution Showcases usually happen near the end of a Unit. During a *Solution Showcase*, you show your classmates your finished product—either your answer to a question or your solution to a challenge. You also tell the class why you think it is a good answer or solution, what evidence and science you used to get to your solution, and what you tried along the way before getting to your answer or solution. Sometimes a *Solution Showcase* is followed by a competition. It is almost always followed by a discussion comparing and contrasting the different answers and solutions groups have come up with. You may be asked to write a report or paper following a *Solution Showcase*.

Update the *Project Board*

Remember that the *Project Board* is designed to help the class keep track of what they are learning and their progress towards a Unit's big question or big challenge. At the beginning of each Unit, the class creates a *Project Board*, and together you record what you think you know about answering the big question or addressing the big challenge and what you think you need to investigate further. Near the beginning of each *Learning Set*, the class revisits the *Project Board* and adds new questions and things they think they know to the *Project Board*. At the end of each *Learning Set*, the class again revisits the *Project Board*. This time you record what you have learned, the evidence you've collected, and recommendations you can make about answering the big question or achieving the big challenge.

Conference

A *Conference* is a short discussion between a small group of students before a more formal whole-class discussion. Students might discuss predictions and observations, they might try to explain together, they might consult on what they think they know, and so on. Usually a *Conference* is followed by a discussion around the *Project Board*. In these small group discussions, everybody gets a chance to participate.

 What's the Point?
Review what you have learned in each *Learning Set*.

 Stop and Think
Answer questions that help you understand what you've done in a section.

 Communicate
Share your ideas and results with your classmates.

 Record
Record your data as you gather it.

PBIS

Diving Into Science

AS A STUDENT SCIENTIST YOU WILL...

PBIS Learning Cycle Actions

Ask QUESTIONS

PBIS Learning Cycle Actions

Pursue ANSWERS

PBIS Learning Cycle Actions

APPLY MEANING

PBIS Learning Cycle Actions

Share ANSWERS

PBIS Learning Cycle Actions

Make MEANING

What's the Big Challenge?

How do scientists work together to solve problems?

Welcome to your new science unit. This unit and the others you complete this year will offer you exciting challenges and opportunities to learn science. Science involves learning very interesting facts, but that's not all science is. A large part of *learning science* is being able to analyze and make sense of the world around you in an organized and logical way. Scientists learn how to do this to be successful at what they do. But scientists are not the only ones who can benefit from this kind of reasoning; you might find it useful too.

In this unit you will learn how to tackle problems and challenges as a scientist does. There is a lot that scientists do to make sure that they solve problems in an organized and logical way. You will experience and use many of these scientific practices. You are not expected to learn everything about being a scientist in just a few weeks, but you will learn a lot. The lessons you learn will help you be more successful in this year's science units. They will also help you in future science classes and even in your life!

Your big challenge is to understand how scientists solve problems. Because this is such a BIG challenge, you will work on four smaller challenges in this unit. Each one will give you a chance to learn a few practices and behaviors. Then you will use what you've learned to answer the big challenge: *How do scientists work together to solve problems?*

Some of you may have already begun learning about what scientists do and how they work together. Therefore, much of this unit will be review. That review will be useful to you. It will give the members of your class a chance to learn to work together. It will also allow you to share what you've learned in other years with your new classmates. You will also find new things to learn in this unit. There is new science content and practices of scientists that you haven't discussed a lot before.

Have fun being student scientists!

Learning Set 1

The Book-Support Challenge

Imagine this scene. You need to copy sections from a textbook into a computer document for a presentation. The job has to be done immediately. You have a computer and the textbook on a low desk. When you sit down and open the book, a problem arises. You forgot your glasses, and you can't read the book.

In the desk drawer you find some index cards, rubber bands, and paper clips. How can you quickly make a book support that will raise the book closer to your eyes?

You will first discuss this problem with your group. Then you will try out some solutions using the materials your teacher has provided. The goal is to support the book at least 7.5 cm (about 3") above the desk. You must be able to read and turn the pages while the book stays on the support.

Your group will have ten minutes to complete a structure.

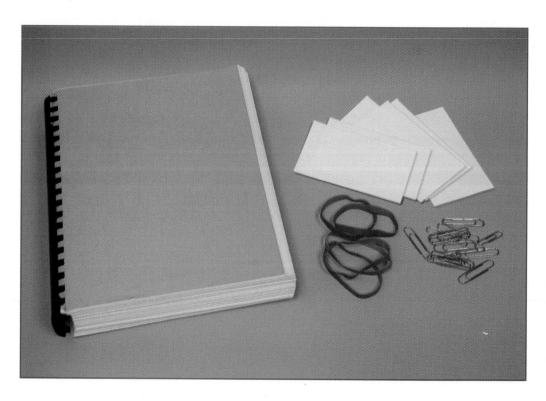

1.1 Understand the Challenge

Identify Criteria and Constraints

Before you start, it's a good idea to make sure you understand what your challenge is. Design challenges have two parts: criteria and constraints.

Criteria are things that must be satisfied to achieve the challenge. For the book support, this will include the job the book support must do. It will also involve how the book support must do that job. One criterion (singular of criteria) is that you must build the book support.

Constraints are factors that limit how you can solve a problem. For this challenge, one of the constraints is that you can only use the materials your teacher gave you. Think about the constraints that have been placed on you for this challenge.

criteria: goals that must be satisfied to be able to successfully achieve a challenge.

constraints: factors that limit how you can solve a problem.

Build and Test Your First Book Support

To help you to begin to think about how to achieve your challenge, you will begin by getting familiar with the materials you will be using. You will also take some time to figure out how the product that you are designing is supposed to function (work). You will get 100 note cards, 50 paper clips, 50 rubber bands, and a ruler. You will have about ten minutes to build and test a book support. As you build your first book support, try out different ideas. Think about which ones seem to work better.

Materials
- **100 note cards**
- **50 paper clips**
- **50 rubber bands**
- **ruler**

Communicate Your Work

Share Your Designs

Your group has built a book support. It is time to share your design with your classmates. Groups should take turns presenting their book-support solutions to the rest of the class. After each presentation, the teacher will test your design to see if it meets the criteria. Then there will be time for classmates to ask questions of the presenting group.

As you present your book support, try to give answers to these questions:

- How is your design constructed?
- Why did you design it the way you did?
- How did the challenge constraints affect the design?
- What things did you think about and try before getting to this design?

As you listen to everybody's reports, make sure you understand the answers to these questions for each. If you don't think you have heard answers to each question, ask questions (like those on the previous page). Be careful to ask your questions nicely.

After each book support is tested, the class should quickly discuss and agree about how well the design fulfills the challenge's criteria.

Update Your Criteria and Constraints

Now that you've tried achieving the challenge, you've found that there is more to think about than you earlier imagined. You may now realize that the criteria and constraints are different than you had first expected. For example, you know that you have to be able to turn the pages of the text while it is on the book support. You will have a chance to design and build a better book support shortly. Before that, review your list of criteria and constraints. Update the list, making it more accurate. A more accurate list will help you design a better-performing book support.

What's the Point?

You now understand what's required for achieving this challenge better than you did when it was first presented to you. People often try to solve a problem without taking time to think about it first. If you do not understand a problem well, your solution won't be the best it can be. In fact, you might fail. Each time you are presented with a new problem, take the time to think. Identify what you have to achieve (criteria). Also, consider what limits you are working under (constraints). You might also find it useful to explore the materials you will be using. You can make a first simple try at a solution. With better understanding of a problem and what is required to solve it, you are more likely to be successful.

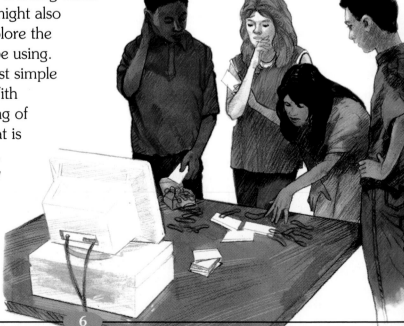

1.2 Design

A Better Book-Support Design

You have already taken some time to explore the materials you will be using. You have built and tested your first book support. You will soon build a better version of the book support. In this science class, you will have many chances to re-engineer solutions to problems or challenges. This time when you build the book support, you will need to record what you are doing. You will also need to communicate your results to others in the class. Before you start, read about the importance of recording your scientific work. You will then have ten minutes to build a working book support.

Materials
- **100 note cards**
- **50 paper clips**
- **50 rubber bands**
- **ruler**

Plan Your Book-Support Design

The first time you built a book support, it was for the purpose of understanding the design challenge. You built it quickly and without a lot of planning. During this second attempt, you are aiming to design and build a book support that really works. Consider what you learned from your first attempt. You might also get ideas by thinking about other products that are similar to a book support. Consider the positives and negatives of each idea. Discuss them with your group members. This will make your design better.

Build and Test Your Design

Now you will iteratively build and test a working book support. Keep records of each **iteration**.

iteration:
a repetition that attempts to improve on a process or product.

Iteration

When people design things, they usually call the thing a product. Often, designers do not create the best or most successful product the first time. Just like you did with your group, they try something. Then they figure out what was good and not good about what they did. They might decide that they need different materials. They might decide that they need to put things together differently. They might decide to make small changes or to make big changes. After the first time, they understand the challenge better. After the second time, they may also find that their solution isn't as good as they'd like. Designers often have to try again and again before they get the product just the way they want it. Each time they try, it's called an **iteration**.

Keeping Records

One very important behavior of scientists is that they record their work as they go. To record means to write, illustrate, or diagram what is being done. This allows scientists to accurately report their findings to others and helps them design future investigations.

You have probably had to keep records of your work in science class before. Keeping records is a very important part of a scientist's job. It is also important for you as a student scientist. Recording your work helps you to do the following:

• Share your work better with others.
• Remember what you did and decided along the way.
• Remember why you decided to do those things.
• Make decisions about what type of investigation to do next.

Recording Your Work

This time, keep track of the number of index cards, paper clips, and rubber bands you use. Record this information on the *Book-Support Records* page. Each of you should fill in your own page.

One of the columns of the *Book-Support Records* page has room for you to draw your design after you have finished building it. You may create additional designs and continue to fill out the page. You will have a record of all the designs you attempted. This will allow you to see how you made improvements along the way.

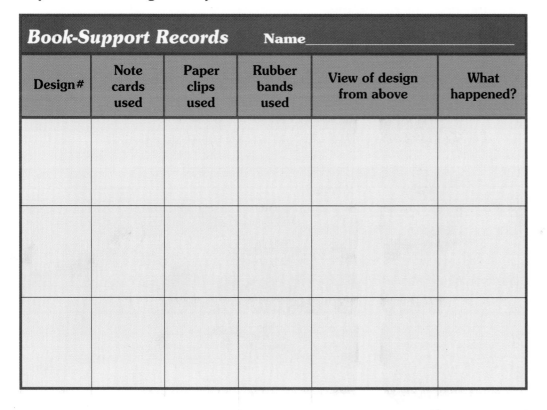

Book-Support Records	Name				
Design#	Note cards used	Paper clips used	Rubber bands used	View of design from above	What happened?

After completing your book support, your group will present it to the rest of the class. During your presentation, have your records page handy to report your quantities to the class.

Communicate Your Results

Solution Briefing

After you designed and built your first book support, you presented it to the class. You will present your new solution to the class too. This time you will present more formally in a **Solution Briefing**. In a *Solution Briefing*, you

Solution Briefing: an opportunity during design and problem solving to present your solution in progress to others and to get advice from them.

DIVING INTO SCIENCE

present your solution in a way that will allow others to evaluate how well it achieves criteria and to make suggestions about how you might improve it. Before you start preparing, read more about *Solution Briefings* on the next page.

As you prepare for the briefing, make sure you can answer questions like these:

- How is your design constructed?
- What materials did you use?
- Why did you design and build it the way you did?
- How does the design meet the criteria?
- How did the challenge constraints affect the design?
- What past experiences helped you make your design?
- What problems remain?
- What things did you try along the way?
- How well does your book support work? What else do you want to test?

Solution-Briefing Notes

Name _____ Date _____ Design Iteration _____

Design or group	How well it works	What I learned and useful ideas		
		Design ideas	Construction ideas	Science ideas
Plans for our next iteration				

As you listen to your classmates' presentations, make sure you understand the answers to the questions above. If you don't understand something, or if they didn't present something important, ask questions. You can use the ones above as a guide. When you think something can be improved, make sure to contribute your ideas. Be careful to ask your questions and make your suggestions nicely. Record the interesting things you are hearing on your *Solution-Briefing Notes* page.

Introducing a *Solution Briefing*

A *Solution Briefing* is useful when you have made one or more attempts to solve a problem or achieve a challenge and need some advice. It gives you a chance to share what you have tried and learned. It also provides an opportunity for you to learn from others. You can ask advice of others about difficulties you are having.

Real-life designers present their designs to each other and to others several times as they work on design projects. A team of designers sets up their design or design plans, and everybody gathers around. They make sure everyone can see. The design team presents their design plan to everyone. The other designers ask questions and give helpful advice about ways to improve the design.

You will do the same thing. In a *Solution Briefing*, each team presents their solution for others to see. Then teams take turns presenting to the class. Other classmates ask questions and offer helpful advice. You might walk around the class from design to design, or teams might take turns presenting in front of the class.

A *Solution Briefing* works best when everyone communicates well. Before you present your design to the rest of the class, think about what might be important to share. What aspects of your design should you present? What parts do you want to discuss with others? You need to be ready to justify to others what you decided to do and why.

When you are listening to a *Solution Briefing* it is important to pay close attention. Look at each design or plan. Think about questions you would like to ask about the design.

Each time you hold a briefing, you will take notes. You will fill out a *Solution-Briefing Notes* page as you listen to each group's presentation.

Collaboration is a group effort. A team of designers share sketches and ideas at the innovation and design firm IDEO.

DIVING INTO SCIENCE

Reflect

Following your *Solution Briefing*, answer the following questions. Discuss your answers and how they may help you achieve the *Book-Support Challenge*.

Draw your group's book support and label the parts. You may find looking at your drawing helpful as you answer the following questions:

1. Why did your group select the features you used in your book support?

2. Which criteria did your design fulfill?

3. What qualities make your book support a good design?

4. What are the problems with your current design?

5. Before the support was tested, what did you think would happen when the book was placed on it?

6. What worked the way you thought it would? What worked differently than what you expected?

Copying versus Crediting

When you build on someone else's idea, it is important to give them credit. Why isn't this "copying?" Copying means taking the work of someone else and claiming it as your own. If you simply build what some other group built, that is copying. But if you add to another group's idea and acknowledge from where you got your idea, you are doing what scientists and engineers do. When you explain how you used their ideas and made them better, you are adding your contribution to theirs.

This means that you will have to keep good records of where you got your ideas. When you use someone else's ideas, always record from whom you borrowed the idea. Record how you included it in your design, and why you did it that way. Then, make sure to give credit to the other person or group in your presentations.

Build on and Benefit from Each Other's Ideas

You ask questions and offer suggestions during a *Solution Briefing*. When you do this, you are **collaborating** with each other. You are working together. You offer your ideas for others to think about. You provide suggestions that might help them improve their solutions. Sometimes you learn something that you want to try yourself.

Other teams may come up with solutions to design challenges that you want to borrow and make better. You may also find that other teams have used your suggestions. Is the other team copying from you? Are you copying from them?

Think about the other team's success as your success when they use something you suggested. Help them see that your success is theirs if you borrowed something from them.

When movie actors receive awards, they often thank many people. Even though they're getting the award, they know that it takes lots of people to put a movie together. It is the same with scientists and engineers.

They wouldn't be able to solve problems or learn new things without building on the work of others. Scientists and engineers write papers, or articles, in journals. They tell others what they have discovered. Others read those papers, talk about the ideas, and ask questions. When someone improves on an idea, they write a paper about it and publish it for others to read and improve. This is the way science is done.

collaborate: to work together.

DIVING INTO SCIENCE

What's the Point?

The book supports you built the second time were probably more successful than the first ones. In general, the more designs you get a chance to build and test, the better your solution will turn out. Each attempt you make is an iteration. Each time you make another attempt, you can do better because you use knowledge gained from the previous attempt. This iterative approach to design and problem solving is what scientists do. Use this approach whenever you have a problem to solve.

You learned that there is a difference between copying and building on the ideas of others. As you took part in the first *Solution Briefing*, you may have seen some design ideas that worked well. You may have used some of those ideas to improve your book support. Others may have used some of your ideas. When you claim someone else's idea as your own, it is copying. If, however, you give credit to the group for their idea, you are building on the work of others. This is how scientists work and how science grows. Science builds on the ideas of others.

You probably have begun to realize the importance of keeping records as you work on a design challenge. You were able to use these records when you presented your ideas during the *Solution Briefing*. You also got a chance to see other solution ideas during the briefing. You saw what works and what does not work as well. This may help you develop better ideas as you continue to solve your challenge. You can learn a lot from attempts that "failed" as well as ones that succeeded. In either case, the goal is to understand the challenge better and create better solutions.

1.3 Read

The Science of Structures

You just finished your first two tries at building a book support. You also talked about the design ideas of other groups. You learned about some ideas that worked well and others that did not. Soon you will work on a revised challenge. Before you do, you probably want to know about the science of structures.

Matter

All objects are made of **matter**. Objects of any form (solid, liquid, or gas) are made of matter. All matter has mass and takes up space. The amount of space that something takes up is its **volume**. The book you are trying to support is made of matter. The matter we are most familiar with is made of extremely small particles called **atoms**. These atoms combine with other atoms to form very small particles called **molecules**. Molecules attach to each other to form the objects that you see, touch, hear, and even taste and smell.

Gravity

You have probably heard of **gravity**. You definitely have seen the effects of gravity. Gravity is a pull between objects. All objects experience this pull towards other objects. The pull between most objects is very small. You usually do not see the objects affected in any way.

However, when one (or both) of the objects is *very* massive (has a lot of matter) you can see the effects. Earth is very massive. There is a pull between Earth and a book. The job of the book support is to resist Earth's pull on the book. It must keep the book from falling toward Earth's surface. Your job is to use the materials you've been provided to construct something strong and stable enough to resist the pull of gravity on the book.

> **matter:** anything that has mass and takes up space.
>
> **volume:** the amount of space that something takes up.
>
> **atom:** a small particle of matter.
>
> **molecule:** the combination of two or more atoms.
>
> **gravity:** a pull between two objects.

Strong Structures

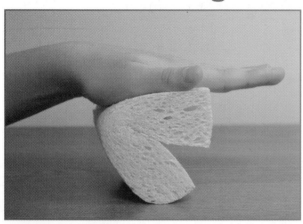

Structures that are **strong** resist **folding** and **compression**. Think about these two characteristics separately.

Imagine a sponge on its end. You can push down on top of the sponge to see if it is strong enough to resist the push of the hand. If the push is hard enough, the sponge will fold over in half and collapse. In the picture you can see a sponge that is unable to resist the push of a hand. The sponge's material folds near the center. Suppose you put a heavy book on the sponge. You probably would see the sponge fold in a similar way.

Now imagine the same sponge sitting flat on a surface. If you were to push the sponge with your hand, it would squeeze into a smaller space. This is called compression. Imagine that the hand were a large book. The sponge would compress a lot.

A sponge is not very strong. It will fold or compress a lot when you put a large weight on it. A **strong structure** will not bend or compress much when a push or pull acts on it.

strong: able to withstand force.

folding: reducing length by bending over.

compression: reducing size by squeezing.

strong structures: structures that resist folding and compressing.

stable: able to resist tipping over.

Stable Structures

Structures are **stable** if they resist tipping over. Again, think about the sponge. Suppose it is sitting on top of a table. In the picture you see that the table supports the sponge well and prevents the sponge from tipping. The sponge is stable. Even though the sponge is partly hanging over the edge, the sponge is still well supported and will not tip and fall to the floor.

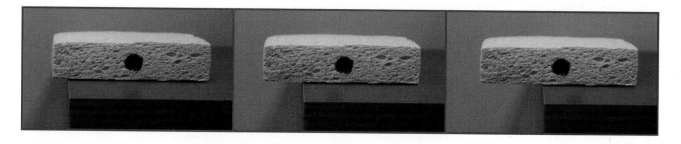

center of mass: an imaginary point on or near an object around which the object's matter is equally distributed.

load: the amount of push or pull a structure has to resist.

What if you keep moving the sponge toward the edge of the table? What will happen? It will eventually fall off. The dot on the sponge represents its **center of mass**. The center of mass is an imaginary point. It is located at a place on or near an object where all of the matter of the object is equally distributed around it. The center of mass of the sponge is in the middle of the sponge, along the line going through the dot drawn on the sponge.

What happens when you move the sponge far enough over the edge of the table so that there is no support to one side or under its center of mass? There is not enough stable support to carry the load. The sponge will tip and fall towards the floor. If the other side of the sponge were supported by a second table, then there would be a stable support.

In the series of pictures you can see what happens when the center of mass moves past the support structure and no additional support is provided. The object will be unstable and will tip over or collapse.

Structures with Columns

Some of you might have found that columns work very well. Columns are very strong structures. They distribute their **load** throughout the column. Load comes from what is on top of something. It is the downward push from objects on top. Distributing the load keeps any one part or area of the column from having to support the entire load.

Load

Support from Entire Column

DIVING INTO SCIENCE

You can think about this in the following way: If you hold an index card flat, with its surface parallel to the floor or tabletop, you can bend the card rather easily.

However, if you hold the card vertically, perpendicular to the floor or tabletop, it is very difficult to fold the ends down toward the floor.

When you roll or fold the index card into a column, it will not compress or fold because it is vertical. Also, it is very difficult for any part of the column to fold in the same direction.

Columns are also very good structures because you can attach them together to make bundles of columns. This achieves two goals:

- The structure is very wide. This means the center of mass of the book has more places to be located over the support structure.

- Many columns, rather than just a few, distribute the load, so each column supports less of the book. This is very similar to lifting something heavy. If you and several friends lift a couch, each person lifts a small part of the load. The more people you have helping, the less of the load each has to lift.

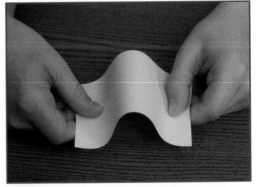

Reflect

Think about the book supports you designed and built so far. Try to think about the science concepts you have read about and discussed as a class. Answer the following questions. Be prepared to discuss your answers with the class.

1. Was your structure strong? If not, did it collapse because of folding, compression, or both?

2. How could you make the structure stronger to resist folding or compression?

3. Was your book support stable? That is, did it provide support so that the book did not tip over? Did it provide this support well? Draw a picture of your book support showing the center of mass of the book and the places in your book support that resist the load of your book.

4. How could you make your book support more stable?

5. How successful were the book supports that used columns in their design?

6. How could you make your book support work more effectively by including columns into the design?

7. Explain how the pull on the book could better be resisted by the use of columns in your design. Be sure to discuss both the strength and the stability of the columns in your design. You might find it easier to draw a sketch and label it to explain how the columns do this.

8. Think about some of the structures that supported the book well. What designs and building decisions were used?

You are going to get another chance to design a book support. You will use the same materials. Think about how your group could design your next book support to better meet the challenge. Consider what you now know about the science that explains how structures support objects.

1.4 Design

Another Book-Support Challenge

Just when you thought you had it all figured out, the challenge has changed! You've realized how useful a book support might be for keyboarding, especially for someone who has forgotten their glasses. Imagine making money selling book supports. What would it take to make your first book support more appealing to buyers, but not be too expensive to produce?

Cost is one of the most important factors that product designers must keep in mind. The cost of your book support is directly related to how much material you use. Assume that each index card, rubber band, and paper clip costs 10 cents. You need to design a low-cost book support that can hold a book in an open position and still allow you to turn pages easily. Once again, keep track of the supplies you use in this final design.

Update Your Criteria and Constraints

Now that the challenge has changed, review your criteria and constraints. Update these lists. Then, consider these changes as you design and build your new book support.

Plan, Build, and Test Your Design

As you design your new book support, you are welcome to use ideas that other groups have developed, but you should make sure to give credit. Once again, keep track of the number of index cards, paper clips, and rubber bands you use in this second design. Record your quantities in the *Book-Support Records* page. Each of you should record this information on your own page.

After completing your book support, your group will present your new solution to the rest of the class. During your presentation, have the record page handy to report your quantities to the class. Good luck!

Communicate Your Solution

Solution Briefing

Now it is time to share your new book support with the class. Once again, you will participate in a *Solution Briefing*.

Like before, spend some time preparing for your presentation. Be prepared to answer questions like the following:

- How is your design constructed?
- What materials did you use, and how many of each?
- Why did you build it the way you did?
- What is the overall cost of the design?
- How well does it work?
- How does the design meet the criteria?
- How did the challenge constraints affect the design?
- What past experiences helped you make your design?
- What problems remain?
- Did you try anything different?
- What else do you want to test?

When you present your book support, your group will need to justify the design decisions you have made and show the results of any other designs you created. Once you have totaled all of the supplies, calculate the total cost of your book support and be prepared to discuss and justify your design and total cost during the *Solution Briefing*.

As before, keep notes on a *Solution-Briefing Notes* page. As you listen to the presentations, remember to ask questions if anything is unclear.

Reflect

Answer the following questions. Be prepared to discuss your answers with your class. Answering the first four questions should help you answer the last one. Your answers to the fifth question are partial answers to the unit's big challenge: How do scientists work together to solve problems?

1. Write the criteria and constraints for the first *Book-Support Challenge* and then for the second challenge.

2. Which criteria and constraints are different in the second challenge?

3. How did you change your original design to meet the new challenge?

4. What criteria and/or constraints were you unable to meet? Why?

5. Define or describe the following ideas that you have learned during the *Book-Support Challenge* and why they were important in tackling this challenge. You may use drawings to help explain your answers.

   a) iteration

   b) collaborating

   c) copying versus building on the work of others

   d) record keeping

   e) using science knowledge

What's the Point?

Now that you've redesigned your book support twice, you have seen again how useful iteration is. Each time you iterated on your design, you had a chance to use what you learned from the last time. Each time, as a result of using new knowledge, you made your book support better.

Sometimes the new ideas you had were based on new science you learned. Sometimes you learned from what other groups had done. Sometimes you remembered experiences that helped you have ideas. Ideas can come from all of these places. It is important, when ideas are borrowed from others, to give them credit. This is how science and engineering make progress. Also, people feel good when others use their ideas and give them credit.

Learning Set 1

Back to the Big Challenge

How do scientists work together to solve problems?

Over the past few days, you and your classmates have been working to create a strong and stable book support. The last book support you built was probably a lot better than the first one. During this activity, you took part in several practices that scientists use when they solve problems. Think about some of the things you did in this *Learning Set.*

You identified the criteria and constraints of your challenge. Criteria are the requirements your solution must meet. Constraints are the factors that put limits on your solution. You also saw how criteria and constraints could change as you attempt to solve the problem.

You learned that there is a difference between copying and building on the ideas of others. You saw some designs of other groups that may have looked very good. In your next attempt, you may have used some of these ideas. Others might have used some of your ideas. This is how scientists work and how science grows as a field. Science builds on the ideas of others.

Scientists work together. They support each other. Working together to build ideas and understanding is called collaboration. In this class, you will collaborate to solve problems or meet challenges. As you collaborate, you will share ideas with others. Others will share ideas with you. One way you collaborated was to participate in a *Solution Briefing*. Scientists often present solutions or ideas while they are trying to solve problems.

Iteration could help you achieve a challenge or solve a problem. You probably saw that it isn't always easy to achieve success the first time you try something. But, once you shared and saw the ideas of others and learned some scientific concepts, you were able to plan and build a better book support. Scientists also use iteration when solving problems.

In this *Learning Set* you probably approached problem solving differently than you have in the past. You now have a better idea of how scientists work together to solve problems.

Learning Set 2

The Sandwich-Cookie Challenge

Have you ever wished that you could have a bite-size version of your favorite sandwich cookie? What would a company that makes these cookies need to know to be able to make a good product? Your next challenge will be to help a company develop a mini-sandwich cookie.

The company needs to know the amount of cream filling that should be placed on each cookie. The cookie must look like it has lots of filling. However, the filling cannot go over the sides.

The important question is this: *How much filling can be placed on the bottom cookie so it is completely covered but doesn't leak over the sides?*

The project is being sent to three labs. At your lab, you are assigned the job of finding how many drops of cream filling can be placed on the cookie without leaking. If your factory is chosen to produce the new product, it will bring in new jobs. It is important that you give this project your best effort!

You will work with a partner on this challenge. You will be given materials to imitate the dropping of cream filling onto the cookie. You will use a penny, a dropping pipette (similar to a dropper), and a cup of water. You will determine how much water fits onto the surface of the penny. Pretend that this is the same as how much cream filling will fit on a cookie the same size as the penny.

2.1 Understand the Challenge

Identify Criteria and Constraints

Before you get started, make sure that you understand what your challenge is. You must understand two features of the challenge: the criteria and the constraints.

Remember that criteria are things that must be satisfied in order to achieve a goal or answer a question. Constraints are factors that will limit how you can go about doing that. Think about and record the goals the company has asked your lab to meet. Think about the limits that have been placed upon you for this challenge (for example, the materials you have available).

What's the Point?

You have been given a new challenge. Remember, to be successful, you need to understand the parts of the challenge. You need to figure out what you need to achieve (criteria). You must also consider the limits you are working under (constraints). By identifying the criteria and constraints, you are more likely to be successful with your challenge.

26

2.2 Investigate

How Many Drops of Water Fit on a Penny?

Materials
- dropping pipette
- 5 pennies
- cup of water
- paper towel

Design Your Investigation

Meet with your partner and discuss a procedure you could use to answer the question: *How much filling can be placed on the bottom cookie so it is completely covered but doesn't leak over the sides?* You will have about five minutes to develop a procedure. Use the materials shown in the list. Record your procedure on a sheet of paper. Each of you should have your own copy.

Run Your Investigation

You will have 10-15 minutes to carry out your procedure. You have five pennies. Your teacher will probably tell you to repeat your procedure five times.

You will need to record your data during this investigation. Remember, recording results allows scientists to accurately report their findings. Data help others understand a scientist's work. They also help other scientists do future investigations.

Record your results on the same sheet of paper you wrote your procedure on. Be prepared to share your results with your class.

Communicate Your Results

Share Your Data

Last time you communicated your work, each group presented in a *Solution Briefing*. This time you'll do it differently. Each group will report their results (number of drops that fit on each penny) to the class. You will record each group's results in a **line plot**.

The line plot will help you see if your class has accurately determined the correct amount of filling for the cookie. This is what the cookie company is looking for.

line plot:
a display of data in which each data item is shown as an "x" above its value on a number line.

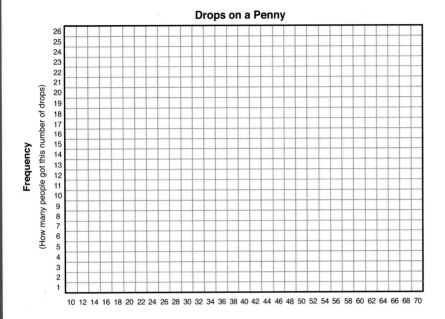

Drops on a Penny

Frequency
(How many people got this number of drops)

Analyze Your Data

Look at the line plot. Answer the following questions. Discuss with your class how your answers may help you better achieve the *Sandwich-Cookie Challenge*.

Have your written procedure available as you answer the questions.

1. Did your group have any problems (mistakes, spills, etc.) during the tests? Describe each one.

2. Did all groups get results similar to yours?

distribution: spread.

3. What did the **distribution**, or spread, of data on your line plot look like? What do you think this says about how reliable your lab's data is? Do you think the cookie company will trust your results?

4. Why do you think there are differences between the data from different groups?

5. How might your procedure and problems you had relate to the differences?

6. What could the class do to get more consistent results in this challenge?

What's the Point?

Most likely the distribution of data on your class line plot was spread very widely. This indicates that the results are not reliable. There may be many reasons why your results varied so much. However, one of the main reasons is that different groups used different procedures. Scientists face this problem too.

To confirm the results of other scientists, they must follow the exact same steps as the original scientist. If a scientist did not provide precise procedures, results cannot be accurately duplicated.

2.3 Redesign Your Investigation

Getting to a Better Procedure

Your class probably did not agree on how much water can fit on a penny. Your line plot may have shown that your lab couldn't produce reliable results. You will now see if you can find a way to make the results more consistent across groups.

Think about what went wrong. You were all trying to answer the same question. You all dropped water onto pennies. You all counted how many drops of water fit on the penny. You also all had the same materials. But every group probably used a slightly different procedure. You all collected data in different ways. No wonder results were so varied.

Scientists only trust experimental results that are **repeatable** by other scientists. In order for other scientists to **replicate** the results of an experiment, the procedures must be reported very precisely. Then someone else can run the procedure again and get the same results.

repeatable: when someone follows the reported procedure, they get similar results.

replicate: to run a procedure again and get the same results.

For example, suppose you wanted to investigate the effect of a fertilizer on the growth of plants. You would need to keep many other factors the same. For example, you would need to control:

- soil type
- time spent in sunlight each day
- amount of water, and
- type of plant

trial: one time through a procedure.

precision: how close together the measured values are.

range: the zone between the largest and smallest solution results.

Think about one factor, water. You would need to make sure that each group of plants got the same amount of water. They would need to be watered the same number of times. Also, they would need to be watered in the same way. You would need to follow these rules for watering every single time you watered each plant.

It is also important to make the same measurement each time. In this example, you could count the number of leaves on each plant. You could also measure the height of each plant.

The tools you use can often affect measurement. You have limits to what you can see when you make a measurement. Be sure to consider how accurate the tools you use are.

Here is a checklist that you can use to make sure your measurements are consistent:

- Measure from the same point.
- Measure with the same units.
- Repeat **trials** for more **precision**.
- Start fresh. Don't compare data from before you make a change to the data after you make a change.
- Measure under the same conditions.

Revise Your Procedure

With your class, work out a procedure for finding out how many water drops will fit on a penny. Try to describe each step in detail so it can be replicated. This way, maybe you'll collect more reliable results. Record your new class procedure.

Reflect

Review and answer the following questions:

1. What are three or four key differences between your previous procedure and the new class procedure?

2. What are you now better controlling in the new procedure?

3. What effect do you think this new procedure will have on the **range** of results across groups?

What's the Point?

The points you thought about in this section are important to the *Sandwich-Cookie Challenge*. Every group was using a similar procedure. However, your procedures were probably not identical. In fact, some of the groups may not have followed the same procedure each time they tested how many drops of water fit on a penny. You probably saw a wide spread of data in the line plot. This is called **variation**. It is important to use the same procedure every time you test. Your results will then be consistent, and they will probably be repeatable.

variation:
a spread of data.

2.4 Investigate

Materials

- dropping pipette
- penny
- cup of water
- paper towel

How Many Drops of Water Fit on a Penny?

Run Your New Procedure

Now that you have a new procedure, can your lab produce more reliable results? Your class will soon collect another set of data and produce a new line plot. As a class, update the criteria and constraints of the challenge if you need to.

Follow your new procedure. Use the materials listed. Obtain results for 5 to 10 trials. (Your teacher will tell you exactly how many to complete.)

Record your results on the same sheet of paper where you wrote your procedure. Be prepared to share your results with your class and teacher. You will have 10-15 minutes to perform your procedure and collect your data.

Communicate Your Results

Share Your Data

Use another sheet of graph paper. Make another line plot from the new data.

As before, each group will read aloud their results. Everyone will plot them on the graph paper.

Analyze Your Data

After your class creates the second line plot, answer the following questions together.

1. How do the results from this investigation compare to the ones from your first set of trials?

2. Did you have any problems (mistakes, spills, etc.) during the tests? List them.

3. Did all groups get results similar to yours?

4. Do you trust these results more? Why or why not?

Revise Your Procedure

Think about and discuss how the new, more specific procedure provides a closer answer to the question: *How much filling can be placed on the bottom cookie so it is completely covered but doesn't leak over the sides?*

You might find that the range of results is still too large for you to trust. If so, come up with fixes to create an even better procedure.

Use this new procedure. Produce a third set of data that is more consistent. Be sure to run your procedure under the same conditions as you did before. You may need to do this part of the activity at home. As before, plot these new results on another line plot. Do you trust these results more? Why?

Reflect

After your class creates the second, or possibly third, graph answer the following questions:

1. What did the distribution, or spread, of data points on your latest line plot look like? What do you think this says about how precise your lab has been at determining the answer to the cookie company's question?

2. Do you think it would ever be possible, given the materials and conditions you have in the classroom, to find an exact answer? Why or why not?

3. What do you think it would take to find an exact answer?

Discuss your answers and how they may help you better achieve the *Sandwich-Cookie Challenge*.

What's the Point?

Revising your procedure was important for your *Sandwich-Cookie Challenge*. By developing a precise procedure for *everyone* in the class to use, your results became more consistent. The cookie company is relying on the "right" answer to their question of how much filling can be placed on the bottom of a cookie sandwich. The more consistent your class results are, the more the cookie company will trust your results.

Learning Set 2

Back to the Big Challenge

How do scientists work together to solve problems?

You and your classmates have been trying to find the answer to a question. In the end, you've probably realized that it would be very difficult to find an exact answer. But as the different groups in the class used more similar procedures, their answers got closer to each other. You found that the way you collect data affects the answers you can find.

The first time everyone tried to determine the number of drops of water that would fit on a penny, each group had different results. That is because each group used a similar, but not an identical, method. The class then came up with a standard procedure. When everyone followed this procedure, the results were closer to each other. Your data became more consistent. You and others could trust your data.

There are three likely sources of inconsistent data:

- Different procedures are used for different trials.

- Factors that can affect the measured result are not carefully controlled.

- The constraints of the tools used.

It is important for scientists that the results of their experiments can be trusted. They must develop very precise methods to use that give similar results each time. Other scientists will want to repeat the experiments to see if they also get the same results. This is the only way that scientists can trust the work of others.

Learning Set 3

The Whirligig Challenge

Cereal companies like to attract attention to their products. One company prints a paper helicopter on the back of its cereal box for children to play with. They call their simple paper helicopter a whirligig. The whirligig is cut out from the box. Parts of it are folded and paper clips are attached. When a child drops the whirligig, it spins as it falls.

The cereal company wants to create a new whirligig that will fall more slowly than the one they have been using. They think that would be more fun.

Your challenge is to determine how to make a whirligig that will fall more slowly than the current one. The company gives you the criteria and constraints.

Criteria

- The whirligig should fall more slowly than the one now on the cereal box.

Constraints

- The whirligig **template** has to fit on the back of the box of cereal.

- The only materials available are the cereal box and paper clips. Assume that people have scissors to cut out the whirligig template from the cereal box.

You'll begin by identifying what you think you know about how things fall. You will then think about what you need to learn more about to be able to achieve the challenge. Then you'll design and carry out experiments to find out more about some of those things. You will also read some science about how things fall. After that, you'll use what you've learned to design a better whirligig. You will need to be able to explain what makes it fall more slowly than the old design.

template:
a pattern.

DIVING INTO SCIENCE

3.1 Understand the Challenge
Thinking about How Things Fall

Demonstration

If you drop a book and a piece of paper at the same time, which will hit the ground first? You may have some ideas about the answer to this question. You also may have some ideas about what affects how things fall. To figure out how to make a whirligig fall slowly, it will be necessary to identify what you think you already know about how things fall. You will also need to identify what you might not understand yet. That way, you'll know what you need to learn to succeed in achieving the challenge.

You are going to observe three short demonstrations. They will help you to figure out what you know and what you need to learn about how things fall. For each demonstration, record your predictions and observations on a *Demonstration Notes* page. Afterwards, your class will share their predictions and observations. You will record the things you think you know and need to learn on a *Project Board*. (You will learn more about the *Project Board* later.)

Demonstration Notes Name_____ Date_____			
Demonstration	**Predict**	**Observe**	**Compare**
#1 Describe the event here.			
#2 Describe the event here.			
#3 Describe the event here.			

During each demonstration, you will be asked to do three things:

Predict – Your teacher will explain to you what he or she is going to do during the demonstration. You will predict what you think will happen. Record your prediction on your *Demonstration Notes* page.

Observe – You will observe the demonstration and record your observations.

Compare – After the demonstration, you will compare your predictions to what you observed. Note what you predicted well and what surprised you.

Conference

Share your predictions and observations with your group members. Make sure everybody has a chance to share. Your predictions and observations probably don't match exactly. As a group, see if you understand why the dropped objects behaved the way they did. Discuss what you think you know and what you thought you knew. Discuss what you think you still need to learn to fully understand your observations. Jot down notes so that you will remember what you discussed when you share again with the class. You will have about five minutes, so get started quickly.

Project Board: a space for the class to keep track of progress while working on a project.

Introducing the *Project Board*

When you work on a project, it is useful to keep track of your progress and what you still need to do. You will use a **Project Board** to do that. It gives you a place to keep track of your scientific understanding as you make your way through a unit. It is designed to help your class organize its questions, investigations, results, and conclusions. The *Project Board* will also help you to decide what you are going to do next. During classroom discussions, you will record the class's ideas on a class *Project Board*. At the same time, you will keep track of what's been discussed on your own *Project Board* page.

The *Project Board* has space for answering five guiding questions:

- What do we think we know?
- What do we need to investigate?
- What are we learning?
- What is our evidence?
- What does it mean for the challenge or question?

Each time you use the *Project Board*, you will record as much as you can in each column. As you work through a unit, you will return over and over again to the *Project Board*. You will add more information and revise what you've recorded. Everything you write in the columns will be based on what you know or what you have learned. In addition to text, you will sometimes want to put pictures or data on the board.

Create the *Project Board*

To get started on this *Project Board*, identify the important science question you need to answer. To design a better whirligig, you need to understand the answer to this question: *What affects how an object falls towards Earth?* Write this question on your *Project Board*.

The demonstrations you just watched were meant to help you remember what you understand about how things fall. They also helped you think about what you don't understand well enough yet. These are exactly the things that you will record in the first two columns of the *Project Board*.

The Whirligig Challenge				
What do we think we know?	What do we need to investigate?	What are we learning?	What is our evidence?	What does it mean for the challenge or question?

What do we think we know?

In this column of the *Project Board*, you will record what you think you know. As you just experienced, some things you think you know are not true. Some things are not completely accurate. It is important to record those things anyway for two reasons:

- When you look at the board later, you will be able to see how much you have learned.

- Discussion with the class about what you think you know will help you figure out what you need to investigate.

What do we need to investigate?

In this column, you will record the things you need to learn more about. During your group conference, you probably came up with questions about how to explain what happened in the demos. You might have figured out some things you are confused about too. And you might have found that you and others in your group disagreed about your predictions. This second column is designed to help you keep track of things that are confusing. Record what you don't understand well yet, and that you disagree about. These are the things you will need to investigate. They will be important for achieving your challenge (designing a better whirligig).

Sometimes you are unsure about something but don't know how to word it as a question. One of the things your class will do together around the *Project Board* is to turn the things you are curious about into questions that you can investigate.

Later in this unit, you will return to the *Project Board*. For now, work as a class and begin filling in the first two columns.

Messing About

Messing About is an exploratory activity. It gives you a chance to become familiar with the materials you will be using. It also lets you figure out how a product you will be designing should work. At this stage, you aren't ready to do a formal investigation or test. When you *mess about*, you explore in a way that will help you do that later.

Mess About with the Whirligig

Messing About: an exploratory activity that gives you a chance to become familiar with the materials you will be using or the function of the product you will be designing.

structure: the way the parts of an item are put together. (This is a different definition of structure than the one you saw while making your book support.)

mechanism: the way the parts of an item connect and move.

To help you think about how to achieve your challenge, you will begin by *messing about* with the whirligig. You will use the basic whirligig that now appears on the back of the cereal boxes.

You will get a template (pattern) of a whirligig. It will look like the one shown below. The whirligig has several parts: blades, paper clips, and a stem. If you call them by those names when you talk about the whirligig, everyone will know what you are talking about.

Cut out the template. To form the whirligig, fold the cutout template. Attach two paper clips to the stem.

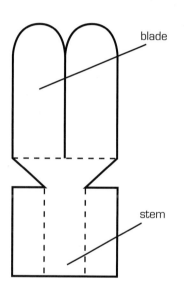
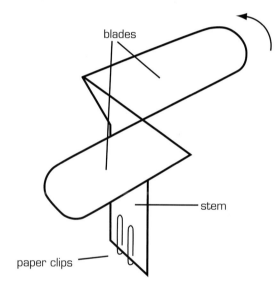

As you *Mess About* with the whirligig, explore how it works. Think about what it is capable of doing. While *Messing About*, see if you can answer the questions below. This will help you identify more about what you still need to learn and help you figure out what investigations to do.

- What is the **structure** of the item I'm working with? (Structure means the way the parts are put together.)

- What are its **mechanisms**? (Mechanism refers to how the different parts connect to each other or move with each other to make the object behave the way it does.)

- How is this item supposed to behave? What might I change in the item to affect that behavior?

You will have about five minutes to construct and drop your whirligig several times. Watch it carefully. Try dropping it in different ways. Try changing some of the parts. Notice the effect these changes seem to have on the whirligig's fall. Discuss the observations you make with your group. Use *Messing-About Observations* pages to record your observations, ideas, and questions.

Messing-About Observations	
Name_____ **Date**_____	
Top view	**Description** (structure, behavior, mechanism)
Side view	**What happened?**

Update the *Project Board*

After you complete a small-group activity, your class will get together to review what you found out and what you were thinking about. This time, you will discuss the behavior of the whirligigs. Update the *What do we think we know?* and *What do we need to investigate?* columns based on your *Messing About* experience.

What's the Point?

In your previous challenge, you identified the criteria and constraints to help you understand the challenge. In this challenge, you were given the criteria and constraints. To help you understand this challenge, you tried to find out what you need to learn more about to be successful.

You made some predictions and observations about several demos. Then you compared your observations with your predictions. You may have found some surprises.

You started a *Project Board* to help track what you understand. You also added questions about how things fall. The *Project Board* is a space to help the class work together to understand and solve problems. Using it will help you have good science discussions as you work on a project.

You *Messed About* with a basic whirligig. You became familiar with how a whirligig moves and acts. This led to identifying more investigations you might do.

3.2 Plan

Whirligig Experiment

You've identified what you need to learn more about to be able to design
a better whirligig. Some of the questions you came up with are about how
different parts of the whirligig affect how fast it falls. It is time now to design
and run experiments to answer some of those questions. You probably
raised a lot of questions on the *Project Board*. Unfortunately, there is not
time right now to investigate all of them. For now, you will focus on only
two of them.

Materials
- **whirligig template**
- **stopwatch**
- **paper clips**

- How does the length of a whirligig's blades affect the time it takes the
  whirligig to fall to the ground?

- How does the number of paper clips on a whirligig's stem affect the
  time it takes the whirligig to fall to the ground?

To answer these questions, you will design and run experiments. Your
group will investigate the effect of either the blade length or the number of
paper clips on how long it takes the whirligig to fall to the ground. Then
you will examine your results. You will try to draw some conclusions from
these results to answer the questions. You can use a stopwatch for timing
whirligig drops.

Variables and Designing Experiments

When you investigate a **phenomenon**, you want to learn about the
factors that influence it. In science, these factors are called **variables**.
For the whirligig, the phenomenon you are studying is what affects
the time it takes a whirligig to fall. The point of most experiments is
to understand how one variable will affect the phenomenon you are
investigating.

phenomenon:
something
that happens.
The plural of
phenomenon
is phenomena.
(The word comes
from Latin.)

variable:
a quantity
whose value
may change
(vary) over the
course of an
experiment.

Design Your Experiment

Half of the class will study how the variable "blade length" affects the time
it takes a whirligig to fall. The other half of the class will study how the
variable "number of paper clips" affects the time it takes the whirligig to fall.

With your group, plan and design an experiment to answer the question that has been assigned to your group. Remember to discuss and record the following aspects of your experiment's design:

Question

What question are you investigating and answering with this experiment?

Prediction

What do you think the answer is, and why do you think that?

Variable Identification

- Which part of the whirligig will you be changing in your experiment?

- Which variable will you manipulate (change) in your experiment to test the effects of that whirligig part?

- What conditions and procedures will you keep the same (hold constant or control) in your experiment?

- What will you measure?

- How many trials will you do for each value of your manipulated variable?

Procedure and Data

Write detailed instructions for how to conduct the experiment. Include the following:

- how you will set up the whirligig

- how you drop it

- how you measure its performance

- how you record the data

- how many trials will you do?

Make sure you can explain to the class why you think they will be able to trust your data.

Use a *Whirligig Experiment Planning* page to plan your experiment. You will have about 15 minutes to plan. Use the hints on the planning page as a guide. Be sure to write enough in each section so that you will be able to present your experiment design to the class. The class will want to know that you've thought through all of the parts of your plan.

Whirligig Experiment Planning Guide

Name:_____ Date:_____

Question

What question are you investigating and answering with this experiment?

Prediction

What do you think the answer is and why do you think that?

Variable Identification

- Which part of the whirligig will you be changing in your experiment?

- Which variable will you manipulate (change) in your experiment to test the effects of that whirligig part?

- What conditions and procedures will you keep the same (hold constant or control) in your experiment?

- What will you measure?

- How many trials will you do for each value of your manipulated variable?

Procedure and Data

Write detailed instructions for how to conduct the experiment. Include the following:

- how you will set up the whirligig

- how you drop it

- how you measure its performance

- how you record the data

- how many trials you will do

Communicate

To help you as you learn to design experiments, you will share your experiment plan with the class. Others in the class have planned experiments to answer the same questions you are answering. You will probably see differences and similarities across these plans. In the class discussion, compare plans to each other. Notice similarities and differences. Identify the strengths of each plan. Think about what might need to be improved in each.

Revise Your Plan

With your group, revise your experiment plan based on the discussion you just had in class.

What's the Point?

You've just designed an experiment to investigate the effect of a variable on the time it takes a whirligig to fall. In the past, you probably followed written steps to run an experiment. Here, you are designing the experiment yourself. Your big challenge is to discover how scientists work together to solve problems. One thing scientists do is collect data and use it as evidence. By designing your own experiment, you will have a better understanding of how scientists do this.

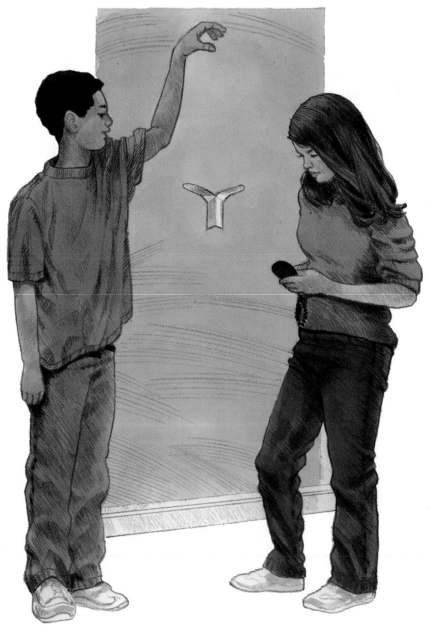

3.3 Investigate

Experiment with a Whirligig

Materials
• cutout whirligigs
• stopwatch
• paper clips

Run Your Experiment

It is time to run your whirligig experiment. Use the materials given in the list. You will run the experiment, analyze your data, and then report your results to other groups.

Recording Your Work

As you do the experiment, record your results on your *Whirligig Experiment Results* page. These pages have guidelines on them. They will help you with each task you need to do. Look at the guidelines for hints.

Whirligig Experiment Results Guide

Name:_____ Date:_____

Data

• Record the results for each trial in a table to keep it organized.

Analyze the data to look for a trend between the variable you changed and the variable you measured. **Hint:** Calculating an average mean or finding the median are two common ways to analyze data.

Quality of Experiment

• How well did your procedure test the effects of the variable you manipulated?

• How well did you control the variables you needed to hold constant?

• How consistently did you follow your procedure each time you ran it?

• How much variation does your data show for each value of your manipulated variable?

If you think you could have done better at any of these, you might need to redesign or re-do your experiment.

Meaning of Experiment

Based on your data analysis write a statement that could be read or spoken as an answer to your research question. Use the trends you see in the data to show how the variable you changed affected the variable you measured. Also use any science knowledge you have to support or explain the answer to your research question.

Be sure to have your teacher check your plan before you conduct any experiment.

Interpret Your Results

Finding Trends and Making Claims

interpret: to find the meaning of something.

trend: a pattern or a tendency.

claim: a statement about what a trend means.

You've collected data about how your variable affects the time it takes a whirligig to fall. It is time now to **interpret** those results. To interpret means to figure out what something means. Interpreting results of an experiment means identifying what happens as a result of changing a variable. What happened as you added paper clips? What happened as you lengthened or shortened the whirligig's blades? Did the time it took the whirligig to fall increase or decrease as the value of your variable increased?

You'll do two things to interpret your results. First, you'll identify **trends** in your results. Then you'll state a **claim** based on those trends. A trend is a pattern that you can see over several examples. A claim is your statement about what those trends mean. For example, suppose you varied the width of the whirligig's blades. You would find that the whirligig takes less time to fall, as the blades get narrower. This is a trend. Your claim would be your statement: "When the blades are narrower, the whirligig takes less time to fall."

Every time a scientist makes a claim, other scientists look for the evidence the scientist has for that claim. One kind of evidence is data collected in an experiment and the trends in that data. You'll spend a lot of time in PBIS units making claims and supporting them with evidence. You'll learn more about that in other units. For now, make sure that the data you collected matches your claim.

Make sure to record on your *Whirligig Experiment Results* page the trends you see in your data. Also include any claims you think you can make so that you can share them with your classmates.

Communicate Your Results

Investigation Expo

You will share what you've found with the class in an *Investigation Expo*.

Remember, no groups in the class investigated both variables. Therefore, others will need your results to complete the challenge. They will rely on your report to design a better whirligig.

Introducing an *Investigation Expo*

An **Investigation Expo** is like other presentations you've done. However, it is specially designed to help you present results of an investigation. You will include your procedure, results, and interpretations of results.

Scientists present results of investigations to other scientists. This lets the other scientists build on what was learned. You will do the same thing.

There are several things scientists usually want to know about investigations. These include the following:

- questions you were trying to answer in your investigation
- your predictions
- the procedure and what makes it a **fair test**
- your results and how confident you are about them
- your interpretation of the results and how confident you are of it.

To prepare for an *Investigation Expo*, make a poster that includes all of the five items listed above. Present them in a way that will make it easy for someone to look at your poster. Others should be able to identify what you've done and what you found out. If you don't think you ran a fair test as you had planned, your poster should also have a report on how you would change your procedure if you had a chance to run the experiment again.

Sometimes scientists make posters when they present their investigations and results. They set up their poster in a large room where other scientists have also set up their posters. Then other scientists walk around the room. They look at the posters and talk to the scientists who did the investigations. Another way scientists share results is by making presentations. For presentations, they stand in front of a room of scientists. They talk about their investigations and results. They usually include visuals (pictures) showing all the important parts of their procedures and results. They talk while they show the visuals. Then other scientists ask them questions.

Your *Investigation Expos* will combine these practices. Sometimes, each group will formally present their results to the class. Sometimes, each group will put their poster on the wall for everyone to walk around and read. In this *Expo*, because you investigated only two variables, every group will put their posters on the wall. The class will look at all the posters. Then two groups will make presentations to the class. One will present for each variable investigated.

Investigation Expo: a presentation of the procedure, results, and interpretations of results of an investigation.

fair test: things that are being compared are being tested under the same conditions, and the test matches the question being asked.

There are two parts to an *Investigation Expo*: presentations and discussions. As you look at posters and listen to other groups present their work, look for answers to the following questions. Make sure you can answer this set of questions about each investigation:

- What was the group trying to find out?
- What variables did they control as they did their procedure?
- Is their data scattered, or is it fairly consistent?
- Did they measure the time it took the whirligig to drop in a consistent way?
- Did their procedure cause them to run a poor, uncontrolled experiment?
- What did they learn?
- What conclusions do their results suggest?
- Do you trust their results? Why or why not?

When looking at posters and listening to presentations, you should ask questions if you can't identify a clear answer to any of the questions above. Ask questions that you need answered to understand results and to satisfy yourself that the results and conclusions others have drawn are trustworthy. Be sure that you trust the results that other groups report.

Different Kinds of Variables

As you designed and ran your experiment, there were several kinds of variables you worked with:

- One you changed or varied in your experiment. This is called the **independent variable** (or **manipulated variable**).

- Some were ones you worked hard to keep the same (constant) during every trial. These are called **control variables**.

- Some were ones that you measured in response to changing the manipulated variable. These are called **dependent variables** (or **responding variables**). Their value is dependent on the value of the independent or manipulated variable.

Experiments are a very important part of science. When scientists design experiments, they think about the things that might have an effect on what could happen. Then they identify the one thing they want to find out more about. They choose this thing as their independent (manipulated) variable. This is the one they change to see what happens. They must keep everything else in the procedure the same. The variables they keep the same, or hold constant, are control variables. Finally, there is a set of things that they measure. This is the dependent (responding) variable. If they have designed a fair test, then they can assume that changes in the dependent (responding) variables result from changes made to the independent (manipulated) variable.

When you ran your whirligig experiments to find out the effects of the number of paper clips on how a whirligig falls, your independent (manipulated) variable was the number of paper clips attached to the stem. Your dependent (responding) variable was the time it took a whirligig to fall. Everything else, including the shape of the blades, the length of the stem, the height from which the whirligig was dropped, and the way the time to the ground was measured were the control variables. To be sure that what was measured (the dependent or responding variable) was dependent on what was changed (the independent or manipulated variable), it was important to keep the controlled variables exactly the same every time the whirligig was dropped.

independent (manipulated) variable: in an experiment, the variable that the scientist intentionally changes.

control variables: in an experiment, the variables that are kept constant (not changed).

dependent (responding) variables: in an experiment, the variables whose values are measured; scientists measure how these variables respond to changes they make in a manipulated variable.

Reflecting

Answer the following questions. Then discuss your answers and how they may help you better achieve the *Whirligig Challenge* with your class.

1. What variable were you investigating in your experiment? What were you investigating about that variable? How did you vary it to determine its effects?

2. List all of the variables you tried to hold constant in your experiment.

3. How many trials did you perform? Explain why you performed that number of trials. Was this a good number of trials?

4. How consistent was your set of data? Why is consistency in repeated trials important in an experiment?

5. Do you think that the data set you collected was useful in determining the effect your variable had on the fall of the whirligig? Explain why or why not.

6. What do you think you now know about how things fall that would allow you to design a better whirligig than the one you started with? Do you know enough to explain your results?

What's the Point?

You have just investigated how a variable affects the time it takes a whirligig to fall to the ground. You then presented your results in an *Investigation Expo*. In your experiment, you only investigated one possible variable. You needed to rely on other groups to get the data you needed for the other variable. This is the way scientists work. Presenting results of investigations to other scientists is one of the most important things they do. This lets other scientists build on what they learned.

You interpreted the data from your investigation. The trends you found and the claim you made will help you in achieving the *Whirligig Challenge*.

3.4 Read

Whirligig Science

Many times you know what will happen in a situation without knowing why. For example, you know that you will not float away as you walk across the floor. What you may not have known is the science behind it. You now know that the science behind why you stay on the floor is gravity pulling you toward Earth. In this section, you will read about the science of why the paper clips and blade length have the effects they do on the way a whirligig falls.

People use scientific information to explain how and why things happen the

way they do. But scientific information does more than tell people why a particular thing happens the way it does. Accurate information also helps you predict what will happen in new situations. You now know how paper clips and blade length affect how much time it takes a whirligig to fall. After learning the science behind these phenomena, you will probably be able to predict things that you didn't investigate. For example, you could predict what will happen if you make the blades of a whirligig wider.

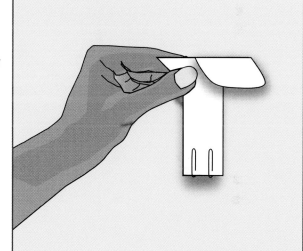

Gravity

You probably know why your whirligig falls toward the ground. It is because of gravity – the same force that you had to consider in the *Book-Support Challenge*. Just as Earth pulled the book toward it, Earth also pulls the whirligig toward it. This pull is called gravity.

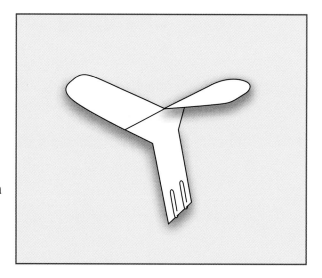

Gravity is the pull between Earth and the whirligig. Even when the whirligig is in your hand, Earth is pulling on it. Your hand and fingers create a pull up on the whirligig. This pull up opposes the pull down of gravity. Therefore, the whirligig does not fall toward the ground. When you release the whirligig, however, your hand is not there to oppose the pull down. The whirligig falls towards Earth.

A Push against Gravity

After releasing the whirligig, there is something pulling it down. You know this is gravity. However, there is also something pushing up against it. You cannot see what this "something" is. It is not your hand. Your hand is no longer touching the whirligig. What is happening is that the blades of the whirligig are falling through the air and bumping into air molecules along the way. These collisions create a push against the bottom side of the blades. Air provides a push on the whirligig that is opposite to the pull of gravity. This opposing push is called **air resistance** or **drag**.

Scientists call pushes and pulls on objects **forces**. Some of the forces you experience are the forces of gravity, air resistance, buoyancy, and friction.

air resistance (drag): the opposing push that resists the movement of an object through air.

force: a push or pull on an object.

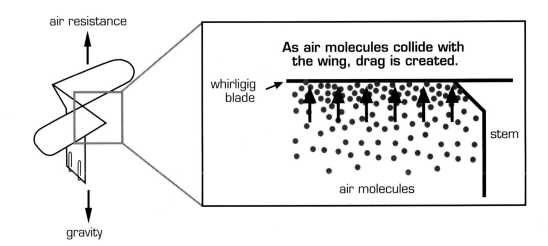

Changing the Push and Pull

When you did your experiment, you saw the effect of two variables on a whirligig's fall: the length of its blades and the number of paper clips attached to its stem. When you added more paper clips, the whirligig took less time to fall. When you made the blades longer, the whirligig took more time to fall.

Stop and Think

Can you use the ideas of gravity and air resistance to explain why?
Think about the following questions:

- Explain how gravity pulls down on a whirligig?

- How does air resistance push up on a whirligig?

- What changes when you add paper clips to the stem? How does that affect the way the whirligig falls?

- What changes when you make the blades longer? How does that affect the way the whirligig falls?

First think about these questions on your own. Then discuss them with your group. After your group meets, you'll have a chance to discuss your answers as a class.

Changing the Forces Due to Gravity and Air Resistance

During the book-support activity you discussed how adding mass (or more matter) to an object increases the force due to gravity that Earth exerts on the object. That is, when you add more matter to an object, there is more stuff for Earth to pull on. The pull on the object is larger.

When you add paper clips to the stem, you add matter to the whirligig. There is more whirligig matter for Earth to pull on, so the pull of gravity is greater. However, the push up of air resistance does not change. Therefore, the overall pull down is larger. You probably saw the whirligig fall in less time as you added more paper clips to the stem.

How does the opposing air resistance affect the time for the whirligig to fall when the length of the blades increases? When you increased the length of the blades, you increased the size, or surface area, of the blades. This increase in surface area results in a greater number of collisions between the air molecules and the blades. A greater number of collisions creates a larger push upward on the bottom of the blades. Thus, increasing the blade size creates larger air resistance. You probably observed this during the experiments. Increasing the blade length increased the time it took the whirligig to fall toward Earth.

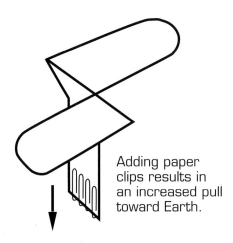

Adding paper clips results in an increased pull toward Earth.

DIVING INTO SCIENCE

Update the *Project Board*

What are we learning and *What is our evidence?*

Earlier you began a *Project Board* centered on the idea of learning more about how things fall. Now you've done some experiments and read some whirligig science. You know more about the factors that affect how things fall. You are now ready to fill in the *Project Board* more completely.

Up to now, you've only recorded information in the first two columns of the *Project Board*. You'll focus on the next two columns now. These are the "What are we learning?" and "What is our evidence?" columns. When you record what you are learning in the third column, you will be answering some questions in the "What do we need to investigate?" column. You will describe what you learned from an investigation you just did. But you cannot just write what you learned without providing the evidence for your conclusions. Evidence is necessary to answer scientific questions. You will fill in the evidence column based on data and trends you found in your investigations. You will also include your understandings of the science readings and your discussions with each other. You may use the text in this book to help you write about the science you've learned. However, make sure to put it into your own words. The class will fill in the large *Project Board*. Make sure to record the same information on your own *Project Board* page.

The *Project Board* is a great place to start discussions. You may find that you disagree with other classmates about what you've learned and the evidence for it. This is a part of what scientists do. Such discussions help participants identify what they or others still don't understand well and what else they still need to learn or investigate.

3.5 Explain

Create an Explanation

After scientists get results from an investigation, they try to make a claim. They base their claim on what their evidence shows. They also use what they already know to make their claim. They explain why their claim is valid. The purpose of a science explanation is to help others understand the following:

- what was learned from a set of investigations

- why the scientists reached this conclusion

Later, other scientists will use these explanations to help them explain other phenomena. The explanations will also help them predict what will happen in other situations.

You will do the same thing now. Your claim will be the trend you found in your experiment. You will use data you collected and science knowledge you have read to create a good explanation. This will help you decide whether your claim is valid. You will be reporting the results of the investigation to your classmates. With a good explanation that matches your claim, you can convince them that your claim is valid.

Because your understanding of the science of forces is not complete, you may not be able to fully explain your results. But you will use what you have read to come up with your best explanation. Scientists finding out about new things do the same thing. When they only partly understand something, it is impossible for them to form a "perfect" explanation. They do the best they can based on what they understand. As they learn more, they make their explanations better. This is what you will do now and what you will be doing throughout PBIS. You will explain your results the best you can based on what you know now. Then, after you learn more, you will make your explanations better.

evidence: data collected during investigations and trends in that data.

science knowledge: knowledge about how things work gathered from reading or research, or discussion that helps you understand why a claim is true.

What Do Explanations Look Like?

Making claims and providing explanations are important parts of what scientists do. An explanation is made up of three parts:

- Claim – a statement of what you understand or a conclusion that you have reached from an investigation or set of investigations

- **Evidence** – data collected during investigations and trends in that data

- **Science knowledge** – knowledge about how things work. You may have learned this through reading, talking to an expert, discussion, or other experiences.

An explanation is a statement that connects the claim to the evidence and science knowledge in a logical way. A good explanation is provided in a way that can convince somebody that the claim is valid.

For example, suppose you live in a city in the USA that gets cold and has snow in the winter. It is fall. You see a lot of birds flying past your home. You wonder why so many birds are flying by. You have learned that many birds cannot live in cold places. They fly to warm places (usually south) to spend the winter. You wonder if these birds are flying by your home on their way to a warmer place. You take out your compass and observe that the direction they are flying is south. You conclude that the birds are flying past your home to a warmer place where they will spend the winter. Look at how you can form an explanation.

Your claim: The birds flying past my house are flying south for the winter.

Your evidence: The birds are flying in a southern direction. (You've observed and measured that using a compass.)

Your science knowledge: Birds that can't live in cold weather fly to warm climates and stay there for the winter.

Your explanation (for why there are so many birds flying south past your house): The birds are flying south to find a warmer place to spend the winter.

An explanation is what makes a claim different from an opinion. When you create an explanation, you use evidence and science knowledge to back up your claim. Then people know your claim is not simply something you think. It is something you've spent time investigating. You have found out things that show your claim is likely to be correct.

Explain

Creating an Explanation

Here is an example from the *Book-Support Challenge*. It might make what an explanation is clearer. When you worked on that challenge, you saw that bundling several hollow cylinders together to make a single cylinder for under a part of a book seemed more sturdy than using a few cylinders, each made out of a single index card, under that part of the book. You then read about how cylinders distribute forces over their whole perimeter, pushing up on what they are holding all the way around. Look at the claim and explanation created by a group of students who worked in the *Book-Support Challenge* and how they derived it.

Solid cylinders, like the columns shown, distribute forces over the entire cross-sectional surface area.

Look at their claim. Remember that a claim is a statement of proposed fact that comes from an investigation.

> **Claim** – a statement of what you understand or a conclusion that you have reached from an investigation or a set of investigations
>
> *Bundles of cylinders provide better support when using weak materials than single or paired cylinders.*

This claim comes from looking at the trend they found in the data they collected.

> **Evidence** – data collected during investigations and trends in that data
>
> *Eight or nine (or even more) cylinders bundled together into one cylinder did not fold or tip as easily as one, two, or three individual cylinders.*

They then read about the science of supports and summarized the science knowledge they learned like this:

> **Science knowledge** – knowledge about how things work. You may have learned this through reading, talking to an expert, discussion, or other experiences
>
> *Supports hold things up by providing a resistance, or push, against the pull of gravity. A support that provides more resistance against gravity's pull will provide better support than one that provides less resistance.*
>
> *A cylinder distributes its push force over 360°.*
>
> *Each cylinder provides a resistance or push against the pull of gravity.*

They came up with this explanation:

> *We recommend using bundles of cylinders to build a book support when using weak materials. Our data showed that eight or nine (or even more) cylinders bundled together did not fold or tip as easily as one, two, or three individual cylinders. We know that cylinders distribute force over 360°, which prevents folding and compression. Also, each cylinder helps hold the book up by providing a resistance or "push against" the pull of gravity. In a bundled cylinder, each cylinder distributes force over 360°. Each resists the pull of gravity on the book. The more cylinders in a bundle, the less gravity each cylinder in the bundle has to resist. Because each cylinder in the bundle has to resist only some of the pull of gravity, the bundle of cylinders is less likely to fold or tip over than individual cylinders, even if a lot of individual cylinders are used.*

This is a long explanation. Long explanations are not always needed. However, seeing this explanation might help you as you try to write explanations. You will also have a *Create Your Explanation* page, similar to the one shown, to help you with explanations. It will give you space to write your claim, your evidence, and your science knowledge. It will also remind you what each of these is.

Create Your Explanation

Name:_____ Date:_____

Use this page to explain the lesson of your recent investigations.

Write a brief summary of the results from your investigation. You will use this summary to help you write your Explanation.

Claim – a statement of what you understand or a conclusion that you have reached from an investigation or a set of investigations.

Evidence – data collected during investigations and trends in that data.

Science knowledge – knowledge about how things work. You may have learned this through reading, talking to an expert, discussion, or other experiences.

Write your Explanation using the *Claim*, *Evidence* and *Science knowledge*.

Communicate

Share Your Explanation

When everyone is finished, you will share your explanations with the class. As each group shares theirs, record the explanation. You might also create a poster for the classroom that has the full set of explanations on it. You will have an opportunity to revise your explanations after you learn more about how whirligigs work and how things fall.

What's the Point?

Science is about understanding the world around you. Scientists gain understanding by investigating and explaining. The results of investigations are useful in making sense of and organizing the world. To help others better understand what they have learned through their investigations, scientists must communicate their results and understandings effectively. Scientists make claims about the phenomena they investigate. They support their claims with evidence they gather during investigations. They also read science that others have written about. They combine all of that together to create explanations of their claims. Other scientists carefully examine these explanations. They discuss them with each other. They try to decide if the explanation is complete enough for them to be sure about whether the claim is **valid**. Scientists accept a claim as valid when many different scientists agree. The evidence and their science knowledge must justify the claim. Scientists also help each other make their claims and explanations better.

valid: well-grounded or justifiable.

Throughout this school year, you will investigate a variety of phenomena. You will apply what you learn to solving Unit challenges and answering big questions. You will be asked to create explanations. Every explanation you write will include a claim, evidence, and science knowledge. As you move through each Unit and learn more, you will create new explanations. You will have the opportunity to edit and improve the explanations you created earlier. Just as you iteratively improved your book supports, you will iteratively improve your explanations.

You will also use explanations you create to help you predict what will happen in new situations. For example, now you know why blade length affects a whirligig's fall the way it does. Therefore, you can probably predict what will happen if you make the blades of a whirligig wider or more narrow. Make sure you can make that prediction. Making that prediction successfully will help you know that you understand the science you've been learning.

3.6 Iterate

More Science and More Explanation

Your experiments showed you that the fewer paper clips on the stem of the whirligig, the more slowly it falls. That is because with more paper clips there is more gravity pulling down on the whirligig. With fewer paper clips, there is less gravity pulling down on it, allowing it to fall more slowly.

What happens when there are no paper clips attached to the stem of a whirligig? You may wish to try this out.

The whirligig probably turned itself upside down and came down quickly.

The reason why is that the paper clips have two effects on the whirligig. They add mass, which results in the whirligig falling more quickly. They also add stability. To understand stability, think back to the *Book-Support Challenge*. You saw that if an object is not balanced, it will tip over. When the whirligig comes down in a vertical (up and down) position, its blades collide with air molecules. In a vertical position, air collides with the blades evenly. This creates a balanced and stable-falling whirligig.

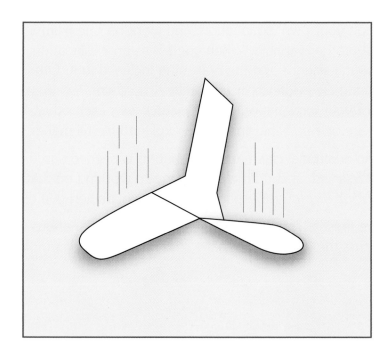

The paper clip on the stem puts the center of mass of the whirligig in a place that keeps the whirligig vertical when it falls. With nothing to keep it vertical as the whirligig falls through the air, it turns downward. When it turns, the blade surfaces no longer collide evenly with the air. There is very little air resistance. Because there is so little air resistance when it turns upside-down, it falls very quickly.

Explain

Sometimes, when you try to apply an explanation in a new situation, you find it doesn't work as expected. This is what happened when you tried to predict what would happen if you took all of the paper clips off of the stem of a whirligig. When you try to use an explanation to design a new solution or make a prediction and you get poor results, it generally means that your understanding of the science is not complete.

This is common in science. Scientists are trying to understand why things work the way they do. They make the best explanations they can as they investigate. But it takes a long time to understand anything completely. Scientists are constantly learning more. They are always revising explanations to make them more accurate and complete.

You have a chance now to do the same thing. Look at the explanations you have created so far as a class. These are the ones about blade length and the ones about paper clips. Work with your group to make those explanations better. Work on your own explanation, and work on one from a group that investigated the other variable. When you revise an explanation, sometimes you will revise the science and the reasoning included in it. Other times you will want to add new evidence or even revise the claim. It is important that all the parts of your explanation work together with each other. Make sure when you revise one part that the whole explanation still makes sense.

If you think an additional claim and explanation is needed based on what you have just learned, spend time in your group working on that too. Use a new *Create Your Explanation* page for each explanation you create.

When you are finished, you will share your revised explanations with the class and discuss the wording, so make sure it is clear and complete.

Reflect

Answer the following questions. Discuss your answers and how they may help you better achieve the *Whirligig Challenge* with your class.

1. What are some other objects that use air resistance to change how they fall or travel? What pull or push is air resistance opposing in your example?

2. The book support uses opposing pulls and pushes to keep the book in place. Here, the whirligig has opposing pulls and pushes, but it does not stay in one place. What would have to happen to keep the whirligig in one place when you released it?

3. Why do you think it was important to return to your explanation to review and possibly edit it? Why might your explanation be a better one by returning to it?

Update the *Project Board*

If the first four columns of the *Project Board* are out of date, spend some time as a class updating it before moving on to address the *Whirligig Challenge*.

What's the Point?

You have learned how to create explanations. You made claims about factors that affect how a whirligig falls. You supported your claims with evidence from your investigations. You also used science that you read about to back your claims. These explanations should help you and others predict what will happen in a new situation.

Sometimes, however, when you apply an explanation to a different situation, it does not work. That is usually because your understanding is not complete. In that case, you need to revise your explanation.

3.7 What Have We Learned?

Back to the Whirligig Challenge

You have raised questions about how a whirligig works and how it could be made better. You then designed and did experiments to begin to find out answers to those questions. Afterwards, you interpreted your results and made some claims. You also read some science that helped you understand more about the whirligig and how it works. Finally, you created and revised explanations to go with each of your claims. You have talked a lot about what affects how things fall. It is time now to identify your answers to how things fall and to apply what you have learned to the *Whirligig Challenge*. What will you tell the president of the cereal company? You will need to make recommendations and justify your recommendations with science. The last column of the *Project Board* is where you record the things that will help you answer your question and address your challenge.

Updating the *Project Board*

What does it mean for the challenge or question?

The last column on the *Project Board* helps you pull together everything you have learned during the Unit. You can then use this to answer the driving question or address the challenge. Each investigation you do is like a piece of a puzzle. You must then fit the pieces together to help you address the challenge. Each piece provides you with a critical factor that must be addressed to answer the big question. Your big question was, "What affects how things fall?" The last column is the place to record what you have learned about the roles air resistance and gravity in affecting how things fall.

recommendation: a claim that suggests what to do in certain situations.

This column is also the place to record **recommendations** about how to address the challenge. Each of the sets of investigations you carried out told you some different things about how to make a slower-falling whirligig. The experiments with paper clips told you about the effects of extra mass or matter on how quickly a whirligig will fall. The experiments with blade length gave you ideas about how they might better shape the blades so that it will fall more slowly. You will pull them together now to make recommendations.

With your class, compose recommendations about how to design a better whirligig. Put them in the last column of the *Project Board*. For each

Making Recommendations

A recommendation is a kind of claim that suggests to someone what to do when certain kinds of situations occur. It can have this form:

When some situation occurs, **do** or **try** or **expect** something.

For example, if you want to make a recommendation for crossing the street you might say the following:

When you have the right of way, **expect** that some cars will not have time to stop in time.

When you have the right of way, look **(do)** both ways to make sure the traffic has stopped.

Recommendations might also begin with "if". For example,

If you have the right of way, and the traffic has stopped, **then** you can cross the street.

recommendation, make sure to identify the evidence and science knowledge that support it (from columns 3 and 4).

Address the Challenge

Your challenge from the cereal company was to create a whirligig that would fall more slowly than the one they have on boxes now. Write a short letter addressed to the president of the company explaining how and why you would change the whirligig. Use what is on the *Project Board* to write your letter – the questions you answered, what you found out, your evidence for those things, the science that helps you explain why you got the results you did, the science that helps you answer the question, and the recommendations about whirligig design that you pulled from your experience. Your letter should spell out specific recommendations you are making about how to change the basic whirligig design to make it fall more slowly. For each of your recommendations, be sure to include the evidence you have that this is a good recommendation and the science you've learned that backs up your recommendation.

You will not be able to make a full set of recommendations to the cereal company right now, because you only investigated effects of extra mass on the stem (the paper clips) and the length of the blades. But you can tell the company president at least a few things about designing a better whirligig for his cereal boxes, and you have collected lots of evidence and read lots of science that you can use to back up what you recommend.

What's the Point?

In the *Whirligig Challenge* there was a lot of investigation, interpretation of results, collaboration with each other, building on each other's ideas, and explaining what you had to do to come up with a set of recommendations that you know can be trusted. As you move through PBIS units, you'll continue to work together the same way you did here. You will work around a *Project Board*, in a way that helps you build on each other's ideas and understanding. There will be lots of opportunities for presenting your ideas and results to each other for discussion and revision.

You moved through the steps involved in understanding how things fall and in designing a better whirligig very slowly. This gave you a chance to see all the different things that are part of doing science: asking questions, making predictions, collecting evidence, interpreting data, reading what others have found out, making explanations, making recommendations, and justifying with evidence. Usually, you'll go through these steps more quickly in other challenges.

You usually won't read science articles until after you have raised questions and experienced a phenomenon. Then the science content will be relevant to what you need to do. Usually, too, you will be examining science for the purpose of addressing some real-world problem. Sometimes it will be a design challenge, sometimes a neighborhood challenge, and sometimes a personal challenge.

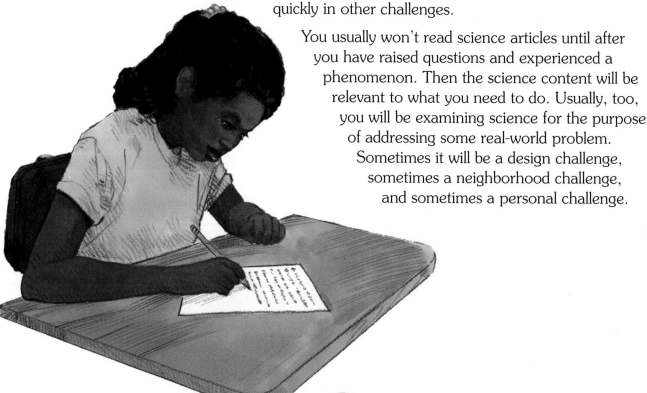

Learning Set 4

The Parachute Challenge

You have learned a bit about how things fall. You will continue learning about how things fall, but this time you will be designing parachutes.

The cereal company took your advice about the whirligig changes. The changes to the whirligig made the toy more fun for children. As a result, the company sold more cereal. Now the company is back again for advice because they trust your input. They want to place another fun toy inside the cereal box. This toy also involves something falling slowly to the ground – a parachute.

The toy is free. Therefore, the cost of the toy to the cereal company must be very low. They want you to make the parachutes out of simple materials. They suggest coffee filters. Also, the slower the parachute falls, the more fun the toy will be. Your challenge is to design, test, and construct a parachute from coffee filters that will fall as slowly as possible.

In groups, you will investigate several variables. You will look at what affects the time it takes a parachute to fall to the ground. Each group will investigate a different variable. You will then present, explain, and defend your work and results to other groups.

As before, you will do this in an *Investigation Expo*. You will then make recommendations for designing and building parachutes. You will explain your recommendations using the data you collect and the science content you learn. With the lessons you learn, you will design and build your best parachute. Then, as a final activity, everyone will drop and time their parachutes. You will see which one falls the slowest and discuss why. This is probably the design you will suggest to the company. Everyone will write a letter to the company suggesting this design and why it is the right one.

This time, you'll move through the steps much more quickly than before. You now know the basics of working together, doing science, and making recommendations. You will use what you have learned before in meeting this challenge.

4.1 Understand the Challenge

Thinking about the Parachute Challenge

Mess About with Parachutes

To better understand the challenge, you are going to *Mess About* with parachutes. Afterward, you will gather around the *Project Board* to discuss what you observed. You will identify the criteria and constraints of the challenge. You will also develop questions you need to answer to address the challenge and to better understand how things fall.

The parachute has several parts. Look at the diagram. Be sure to use the correct names when you talk about these parts.

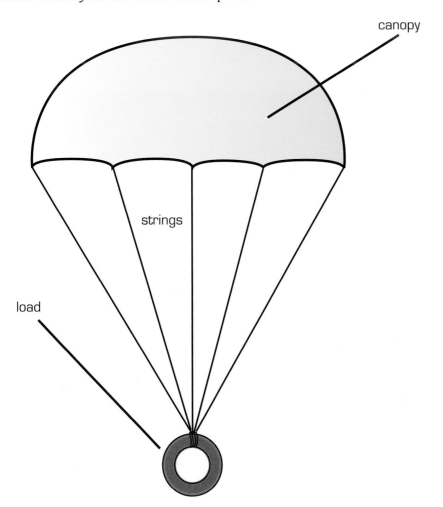

Materials
- **coffee filters**
- **string**
- **washers**
- **transparent tape**
- **stopwatch**

Obtain the materials to make a basic parachute. These include coffee filters, strings, tape, and washers. Look at the model parachute presented by your teacher. You will have about ten minutes to construct a similar parachute and drop it several times. Remember, *Messing About* means exploring how something looks or works. You will have a chance to figure out the structure, behavior, and mechanisms of the parachute. In this case, you are *messing about* to try to figure out what variables might affect how quickly or slowly a parachute falls.

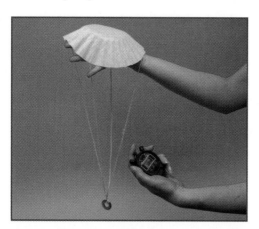

Use a *Messing-About Observations* page. Record your observations, ideas, and questions. Then list the variables that you think you might be able to test to determine their effect on a parachute's fall. Remember that the purpose of *messing about* is to figure out what you need to investigate or learn more about.

Messing-About Observations

Name_____ Date_____

Top view	Description (structure, behavior, mechanism)
Side view	**What happened?**

Identify Criteria and Constraints

Criteria are what you need your parachute to be able to do. Constraints are the limitations you have to keep in mind as you design it. It is always a good idea to identify criteria and constraints when working on a design challenge. That way, you have a way of checking which of your ideas are worth spending more time on. You can also identify which ideas are not worth spending time on. List and discuss the criteria and constraints.

Revise the *Project Board*

When you were designing your whirligigs, you raised the question: *What affects how an object falls towards the ground?* You already know some things about the answer to this question. You wrote them on the *Project Board* you used for the *Whirligig Challenge*. You will be addressing the same question for this challenge. Therefore, you will continue to use the same *Project Board*.

There will be some things on the board that are specific to whirligigs. You won't use them in this challenge. But, you will find that much of what is on the board is relevant to designing your parachutes. Now that you've *messed about* with parachute materials, you probably have some new ideas about how to answer this question. You also may have some smaller questions you need to answer to determine what affects how a parachute falls towards the ground. Now is a good time to return to the *Project Board*.

To begin, as you did before, you will review what you think you know about falling objects. As a result of your work with whirligigs, you know more now than you did a week ago. You should also include in the "What do we think we know?" column what you think you know about parachutes and how they fall.

As you noticed while working on the *Whirligig Challenge*, some of your observations might have confused you. These questions go into the "What do we need to investigate?" column. Now that you know about variables, try to write some of these questions so that they ask about the effects of variables on how something falls. For example, you have probably seen parachutes in the movies or on TV. They are not all the same shape. You might want to ask one of these questions (or both):

- *How does the shape of the parachute's canopy affect how fast a parachute falls?*

- *How does the shape of the parachute's canopy affect the path it takes as it falls?*

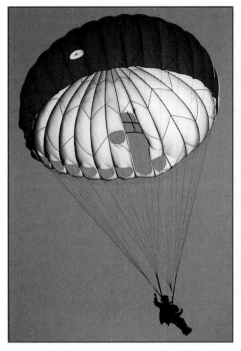

What's the Point?

Through *messing about*, you became familiar with the way parachutes work. You developed a feel for the materials you will use later. You were also able to identify some of the variables that might affect how slowly a parachute will fall. This allowed you to do two things:

- Identify the criteria and constraints of the challenge (what you need to accomplish and the limitations).

- Identify questions you need to investigate to be able to design the best parachute.

In your class discussions around the *Project Board* you made a list of factors that would be appropriate to investigate. Different groups came up with different ideas of what affects a parachute's fall. It was only by collaborating (working together) as a class that you were able to record a full set of questions about how the parachute might work.

It is important to remember two earlier lessons:

- *Messing About* can help you understand the problem you are trying to solve or the question you are trying to answer. It is important to begin to understand a problem before trying to solve it. You should identify exactly what you need to learn more about before attempting a solution or answer.

- A *Project Board* is a good tool to use to keep track of what you need to be doing and what you are learning.

Now that you've identified the questions you need to answer, you know what you need to do next. You need to investigate to find the answers to some of those questions.

4.2 Investigate

Investigate Parachutes

Materials
- **coffee filters**
- **string**
- **washers**
- **transparent tape**
- **stopwatch**

You have just identified variables that might make a difference in the way a parachute will fall. You've also recorded questions about the effects of those variables on the *Project Board*. Now it is time to find the answers.

Design Your Experiment

Each group will investigate the effects of a different variable on how a parachute falls. In your group, discuss and then design a good experiment to investigate the effects of your variable on a parachute's fall. You will want an answer to your question that you can trust. Therefore, it is important to remember the lessons you learned while experimenting with the whirligig. Here is a list of reminders to help you organize your thinking.

Question

What question are you investigating and answering with this experiment?

Prediction

What do you think the answer is, and why do you think that?

Variable Identification

- Which part of the parachute will you be changing in your experiment?
- Which variable will you manipulate (change) in your experiment to test the effects of that parachute part?
- What conditions and procedures will you keep the same (hold constant or control) in your experiment?
- What will you measure?
- How many trials will you do for each value of your manipulated variable?

Procedure and Data

Write detailed instructions for how to conduct the experiment.
Include the following:
- how you set up the parachute
- how you drop it
- how you measure its performance
- how you record the data
- how many trials will you do?

Have your teacher check your plan before you run your experiment.

Use the *Parachute Experiment Planning Guide* and *Parachute Experiment Results Guide* to help you plan and organize your experiment.

Parachute Experiment Planning Guide

Name:_____ Date:_____

Question
What question are you investigating and answering with this experiment?

Prediction
What do you think the answer is, and why do you think that?

Variable Identification

• Which part of the parachute will you be changing in your experiment?

• Which variable will you manipulate (change) in your experiment to test the effects of that parachute part?

• What conditions and procedures will you keep the same (hold constant or control) in your experiment?

• What will you measure?

• How many trials will you do for each value of your manipulated variable?

Procedure and Data

Write detailed instructions for how to conduct the experiment. Include the following:

• how you will set up the parachute

• how you drop it

• how you measure its performance

• how you record the data

• how many trials you will do

Parachute Experiment Results Guide

Name:_____ Date:_____

Data
• Record the results for each trial in a table to keep it organized.
Analyze the data to look for a trend between the variable you changed and the variable you measured. **Hint:** Calculating an average mean or finding the median are two common ways to analyze data.

Quality of Experiment

• How well did your procedure test the effects of the variable you manipulated?

• How well did you control the variables you needed to hold constant?

• How consistently did you follow your procedure each time you ran it?

• How much variation does your data show for each value of your manipulated variable?

If you think you could have done better at any of these, you might need to redesign or re-do your experiment.

Meaning of Experiment
Based on your data analysis write a statement that could be read or spoken as an answer to your research question. Use the trends you see in the data to show how the variable you changed affected the variable you measured. Also use any science knowledge you have to support or explain the answer to your research question

Run Your Experiment

Gather the materials you need to run your experiment. Follow the procedure you developed carefully. Record your data. Identify any trends that you see in your data. After you have completed your experiment, you will present your procedure and results in an *Investigation Expo*.

Communicate Your Results

Investigation Expo

When you finish your experiment, you will share your results with the class in an *Investigation Expo*. In this *Expo*, each group will take turns standing in front of the class and presenting their experiment design and results. So that others will be able to learn from what you did and will be able to use your results when they design their best parachute, you will make a poster that includes the procedure you followed, your data, and the meaning of your results. Your poster should include five kinds of information:

- questions you were trying to answer in your investigation
- your predictions
- the procedure and what makes it a fair test
- your results and how confident you are about them, and
- your interpretation of the results and how confident you are of it

You might find out after running your experiment that you did not control variables well enough. If you find that, don't worry right now. You will have another chance. But do be honest about it. If you think the test you ran was not as fair as you had planned, say so. Then explain how you would change your procedure if you had a chance to run the investigation again.

Now you should be ready to discuss your results. Use your poster to present your experiment and results to the class. Like you did in the whirligig activity, take notes as others present. Look for answers to these questions in each presentation:

- What was the group trying to find out?
- What variables did they control as they did their procedure?
- Is their data scattered, or is it fairly consistent?
- Did they measure the time it took the parachute to drop in a consistent way?
- Did their procedure cause them to run a poor, uncontrolled experiment?
- What did they learn?
- What conclusions do their results suggest?
- Do you trust their results? Why or why not?

Each group in the class investigated effects of a different variable. Therefore, each group will have a chance to present their experiment and results to the class. Make sure you can answer these questions for each presentation. If you cannot, ask questions of the group that is presenting. It will be important for you to trust the results of other groups in the class. You will need these results to fully address the *Parachute Challenge*.

Revise Your Experiment

Do you trust all of the results that were presented? Probably not. Why do you not trust *every* groups' results? Some groups might not have managed variables well and some groups might have run their procedures inconsistently. Maybe some measured in a way that was inconsistent across trials. What made you think you could not trust some groups' results? Probably their data were too scattered or inconsistent.

What should you do now if the class does not trust *every* groups' results? Remember why you are running these experiments. Every group is running an experiment to investigate the effects of one variable on a parachute's fall. If you cannot trust results about a variable's effects, then you will not know what to do about that variable when you design *your* best parachute. For example, if a group that investigated the effects of the surface area of the canopy did not produce results you trust, then how will you know what size the canopy on your parachute should be?

If you cannot trust the results of every groups' investigation, then you probably should have those groups rerun their experiments. This time the group should manage the variables and procedures better. While they are doing that, the other groups can investigate to find the answer to some question on the *Project Board* that has not been investigated yet. After running yor experiments again, you will hold another *Investigation Expo*. Follow the instructions you followed for the *Investigation Expo* you just completed.

Reflect

Think about and answer the following questions. Later, your class will discuss your answers and how they may help you better achieve the *Parachute Challenge*.

1. What was the variable you were testing during your experiment? Explain how you were able to change the variable you were testing in order to determine its effect.

2. List all of the variables you controlled (did not change) during your experiment.

3. How many trials did you perform? Explain why you performed that number of trials.

4. How consistent was your set of data? Why is consistency in repeated trials of testing important in an experiment?

5. Do you think that the data set you collected was useful in determining the effect the variable had on the fall of the parachute? Explain why or why not.

What's the Point?

During the *Investigation Expos* you presented the results of your experiment to the class. You also listened as others presented their results. They investigated different variables than you did. Therefore, it was very important for you to listen carefully to their presentations. It was also very important to you that their data sets were consistent. You are counting on their results to produce the best parachute possible. Scientists work in the same way. They rely on the experiments of other scientists to further their research.

4.3 Explain and Recommend

Explanations and Recommendations about Parachutes

As you did after your whirligig experiments, you will spend some time now explaining your results. You will also try to come up with recommendations. Remember that explanations include your claims, the evidence for your claims, and the science you know that can help you understand the claim. A recommendation is a special kind of claim where you make a statement about what someone should do. The best recommendations also have evidence, science, and an explanation associated with them. In the *Whirligig Challenge*, you created explanations and recommendations separately from each other. This time you will work on both at the same time.

Create and Share Your Recommendation and Explanation

Work with your group. Use the hints on the *Create Your Explanation* pages to make your first attempt at explaining your results. You'll read about parachute science later. After that, you will probably want to revise your explanations. Right now, use the science you learned during the *Whirligig Challenge* for your first attempt.

Write your recommendation. It should be about designing a slow-falling parachute. Remember that it should be written so that it will help someone else. They should be able to apply what you have learned about the effects of your variable. If you are having trouble, review the example in *Learning Set 3*.

Create Your Explanation

Name:_____ Date:_____

Use this page to explain the lesson of your recent investigations.

Write a brief summary of the results from your investigation. You will use this summary to help you write your Explanation.

Claim – a statement of what you understand or a conclusion that you have reached from an investigation or a set of investigations.

Evidence – data collected during investigations and trends in that data.

Science knowledge – knowledge about how things work. You may have learned this through reading, talking to an expert, discussion, or other experiences.

Write your Explanation using the *Claim*, *Evidence* and *Science knowledge*.

When you are finished, you will share your explanations and recommendations with the class. As each group shares theirs, keep track on your own *Create Your Explanation* pages.

What's the Point?

Science is about understanding the world around you. Scientists learn about the world by doing investigations. They make claims and provide explanations based on their evidence and the science they already know. Then they communicate their results to other scientists.

Throughout this school year, you will investigate a variety of phenomena. You will apply what you learn to answering big questions and achieving challenges. You will be asked to explain your understandings and knowledge many times during each unit. You will write and share your understanding in explanations. Then you will make recommendations from the explanations you have created. As you move through each unit, you will have many opportunities to edit and improve your explanations and recommendations.

4.4 Read

Parachute Science

You have been experimenting with parachutes. You determined the effect different variables have on the way the parachute falls. In previous sections, you have looked at how pulls and pushes can affect how whirligigs fall. In this section, you will see that pulls and pushes affect how your parachute falls as well.

Gravity and Air Resistance...Again

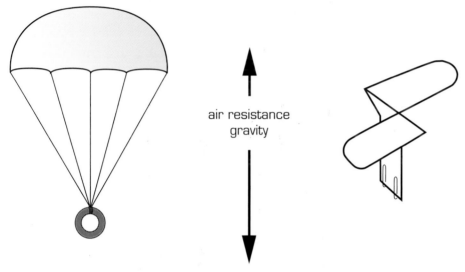

air resistance
gravity

The parachute falls towards the ground because gravitational force is greater than force from air resistance at the time of dropping. As time passes these forces become equal in length.

It is probably obvious to you by now that parachutes work according to the same scientific principles as the whirligig. Gravity pulls the parachute toward the ground. The canopy of the parachute collides with air molecules. These collisions create air resistance. The air pushes up on the parachute. In both the whirligig and the parachute, the pull of gravity is greater than the push up of air resistance. That is why both end up falling toward the ground.

What is different in parachutes and whirligigs are their parts. This affects the kinds of changes you can make in their designs. In turn, the changes affect how quickly the parachute falls toward Earth.

In the whirligig...

- when you adjusted the number of paper clips, you were adjusting the downward pull of gravity. More paper clips created more pull.

- when you adjusted the length of the wings, you adjusted the upward push of air. Longer wings have more surface area. This creates more air resistance and more upward push.

Consider what affects the pushes, pulls, and balance of a parachute.

These forces occur at or very near the time of dropping the parachutes. As time passes these forces become equal in length.

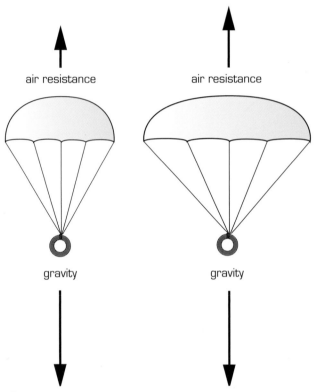

Canopy Size

Changing the size of a parachute's canopy is very similar to changing the length of a whirligig's wings. Increasing the size of the canopy increases the surface area of the canopy. This will increase the number of air molecules the canopy collides with. This increase in collisions produces more upward pushes on the canopy. This increases the upward push on the parachute.

By increasing the air resistance, or drag, you can create a parachute that will fall more slowly. But because of the shape of a parachute, there is a limit to how big its canopy should be. When the canopy is very big, it is difficult for the parachute to remain balanced as it falls. When the parachute is not balanced, it will tip to one side. Then it will topple and fall to the ground.

Number of Washers

A parachute's washers are like paper clips on the whirligig. When you add washers to a parachute, you are increasing the total amount of matter in the parachute. Thus, adding washers to the parachute's load (what it carries) increases the pull of gravity acting on the parachute.

Consider what would happen if you removed all the washers from a parachute. The force of gravity would be greatly reduced. The air resistance would not change. You might think that the parachute would fall really slowly. But something else happens. If you try it, you will see the canopy collapses. The parachute falls quickly. You might also see the canopy (coffee filter) turn itself over. The parachute's load plays an important role in its stability. It is similar to what the paper clips do for the whirligig. They help the parachute stay upright. When the parachute is not upright, the upward push of air on the parachute is uneven. This causes it to turn over or fall quickly to the ground.

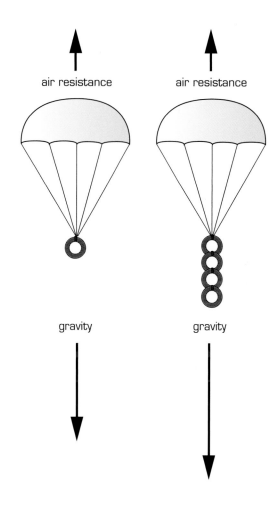

String Length

The strings on a parachute support the parachute's load. They keep it connected to the canopy. They also do another important job. The lengths of the strings on a parachute determine the shape of the parachute in two ways:

- They control how far below the canopy the load hangs.
- They control how far right or left of the parachute's center the load hangs.

Suppose the load is close to the canopy. Air resistance pushing up on the canopy can easily flip the parachute over. Increasing the distance between the load and the canopy makes the parachute more stable. But suppose

DIVING INTO SCIENCE

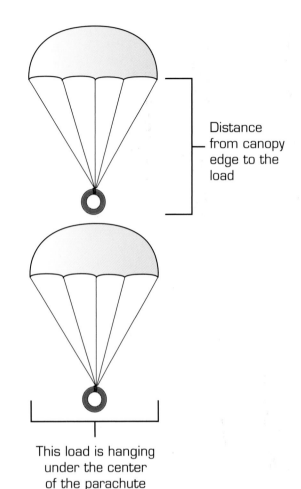

Distance from canopy edge to the load

This load is hanging under the center of the parachute

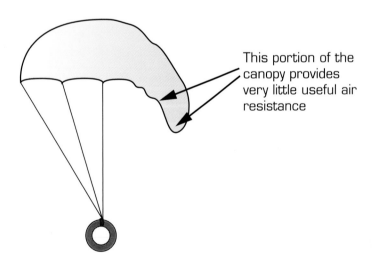

This portion of the canopy provides very little useful air resistance

the load hangs too far from the canopy? The canopy will not fully inflate. This reduces the amount of air resistance. The distance from the edge of the canopy to the load should be just a bit longer than the diameter of the canopy.

In order to have a balanced and stable parachute, the strings must keep the load (the washers) under the center of the parachute. This requires that each string be the same length. They should also be connected to the canopy at equal distances from the canopy's edge.

Number of Strings

A parachute's strings also help to evenly distribute air resistance around the canopy. Suppose one area of the canopy is left unsupported. Air will flow out of that area, and there will be lower air resistance in that part of the parachute.

A small number of strings can produce an uneven push upward. This can lead to a quicker falling time. It also makes the parachute unstable. Too many strings can also cause a problem. They can become tangled during the fall. The correct number of strings depends on the material and shape of the canopy.

Canopy Vents

Many parachutes have vent holes. Vents control how the air passes through and around the canopy. As air enters and runs into the canopy, it behaves much like water if you were pouring it from one bucket into another. The air strikes the surface of the canopy and is redirected. It will slosh around inside the canopy, especially as new air molecules continue to enter the canopy area.

This new air will push old air over and out of the canopy's edge. This is very similar to how water would move if you were pouring a large amount of it, quickly, into a shallow sink with the stopper closed.

Adding vent holes helps reduce the sloshing of air. This results in a more stable fall. There is, however, a tradeoff. Cutting holes in the canopy reduces the amount of air resistance. Vent holes can be useful. However, the number of vent holes has to provide balance between increased stability and decreased air resistance.

Canopy Shape

You know that the canopy provides air resistance that pushes up on the parachute. The upward push offsets the downward pull of gravity. This causes the parachute to fall slowly. The shape of the canopy can also have an effect. However, it is the size of the canopy and the balance of the canopy that affect this variable. The surface area of the canopy is the key factor, not the shape. It is possible to have a circular canopy and a triangular canopy with equal surface areas. The difference is that it is easier to evenly distribute the strings around a circle. This creates a more balanced upward push of air resistance.

Some parachutes are designed to slice through the air like an airplane wing. The canopies are rectangular. They look like wings. They allow a parachutist to control the path of the parachute.

Review and Revise Explanations and Recommendations

You've just read about how gravity and air resistance are involved in the fall of a parachute. With your group, look at the explanation and recommendation you created after your parachute experiment. Use the science content you read about to support your claims. Edit your claims as needed and rewrite them. Make sure your previous explanation and recommendation are consistent with the science you just learned.

When you are finished, you will once again share your explanations and recommendations with the class.

Update the *Project Board*

Now that you've run parachute experiments and learned some of the science of parachutes, you are ready to revise the *Project Board* once again. You will focus on "What are we learning?," "What is our evidence?," and "What does it mean for the challenge or question?"

Remember that the claims you record in the "What are we learning?" column come from your investigations. You saw how a variable affects the fall of a parachute. Make sure to include in the "What is our evidence?" column all of the evidence you have (data, trends, science) that supports each claim. In the "What does it mean for the challenge or question?" column, revise your answers to the question, *What affects how objects fall towards Earth?* Revise recommendations about designing a slowly falling parachute. For more advice about what goes in these columns, look back at *Learning Set 3*. Don't forget to update your personal *Project Board*.

Reflect

Think about and answer the following questions. Later, your class will discuss your answers and how they may help you better achieve the *Parachute Challenge*.

1. What are some other objects that use air resistance to change how they fall or travel? What pull or push is air resistance opposing in your example?

2. The book support uses opposing pulls and pushes to keep the book in place. Here, the parachute has opposing pulls and pushes, but it does not stay in one place. What would have to happen to keep the parachute in one place when released?

3. Why do you think it was important to return to your "What are we learning?" and "What does it mean for the challenge or question?" columns? You had filled things in those columns during the *Whirligig Challenge*. Why were you able to revise those columns now?

4.5 Plan

Design a Slow-Falling Parachute

While working on the *Whirligig Challenge*, you made recommendations. However, you did not have a chance to test them. This time, you are going to use all the recommendations that the class made to design and test a parachute. You are not just giving the cereal company advice about making a better parachute. You are giving them advice about how to design their first one.

Plan

As you read about parachute science, you read about trade-offs. For example, longer strings are good up to a point. However, strings that are too long get tangled. More strings are also good. Yet too many strings make the parachute hard to build. These real-world issues are important to consider along with the science as you work on designing a good parachute for putting inside a cereal box.

You have learned a lot about how a variety of variables affect the fall of a parachute. You have also learned a lot about the science of falling. With your group, design your best parachute. Plan one you think will fall as slowly as possible. Make decisions together about how to set each of the variables in your parachute. How long will your strings be? How much load will your parachute carry? How many coffee filters will you use in the canopy? How will you shape the canopy? What will be the surface area of the canopy? For each design decision you make, know why you are making that decision. Record what evidence you are using to make each decision. Your decisions should be informed by the evidence you have available.

When you are finished, you will have a chance to share your plan with other groups in a *Plan Briefing* before you actually build and test your design. Others in the class might be able to help you with any difficult decisions you need to make as you work on your design plan.

Communicate Your Plan

Plan Briefing

As you are finishing your design plan, begin to draw a poster for presentation of your design plan to the class. Your teacher will provide you with a large sheet of paper to create your *Plan-Briefing* poster and possibly a template to follow. You will have 20 minutes to create a *Plan-Briefing* poster and organize your presentation.

Your teacher will then lead your class through a *Plan-Briefing* session.

Introducing a *Plan Briefing*

Preparing a *Plan-Briefing* Poster

A *Plan Briefing* is very much like the other presentations you have learned to do. In a *Plan Briefing*, you present your design plan. You must present it well enough so that your classmates can appreciate your ideas. They should be able to identify if you have made any mistakes in your reasoning. Then they can provide you with advice before you begin constructing your parachute. As a presenter, you'll learn the most from a *Plan Briefing* if you can be very specific about your design plans and about why you made your design decisions. You'll probably want to draw pictures, maybe providing several views. You certainly want everyone to know why you expect your design to achieve the challenge.

The following guidelines will help you as you decide what to present on your poster:

- Your poster should have a detailed drawing of your design with at least one view. You might consider drawing multiple views so that the audience can see your design from different angles. It is important that the audience can picture what you are planning to build.

- Parts of the design and any special features should all be labeled. The labels should describe how and why you made each of your design decisions. Show the explanations and recommendations that support your decisions. Convincing others that your design choices are quality ones means convincing them that you are making informed decisions backed by scientific evidence.

- Make sure to give credit to groups or students who ran the experiments that inform your design and who gave you ideas.

If another group experimented with and provided an *Explanation* or a

---

Recommendation that you are using, you should credit them with their assistance in developing your final design.

Participating in a *Plan Briefing*

A *Plan Briefing* is very much like an *Investigation Expo* and a *Solution Briefing*. However, this time you will be presenting your design plan. As in other presentation activities, groups will take turns making presentations. After each presentation, the presenting group will take comments and answer questions from the class.

When presenting, be very specific about your design plan and what evidence helped you make your design decisions.

Your presentation should answer the following questions:

- What are the features of the design?
- For each, what criterion will it achieve? Why is this the right way to achieve that criterion?
- Are there any problems you foresee with this design?
- What do you predict will happen when you release your parachute?
- Is there anything you need help with?

As a listener, you will provide the best help if you ask probing questions about the things you don't understand. Be polite when you point out errors and misconceptions in the reasoning of others. These kinds of conversations will allow listeners to learn as well.

For each presentation, if you don't think you understand the answers to the questions above, make sure to question your classmates. When you ask them to clarify what they are telling you, you can learn more. They can learn, too, by trying to be more precise.

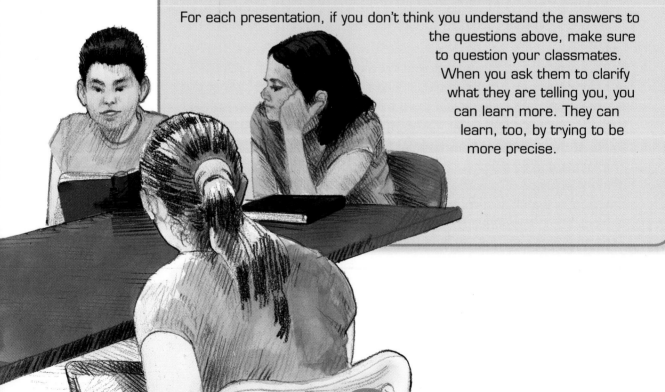

Revise Your Plan

You may have received some good advice from classmates about how to revise your design plan to make it better. If so, spend some time with your group doing that. Be sure to update the pages you are using to record your plan and to justify your design decisions.

What's the Point?

Do you have a strong opinion about something? Many people do. They assume that their points of view are obvious to others. They tend to think that other people will automatically hold those same views. But often you will be surprised. What was obvious to you looks different to someone else. You struggle with this all the time. What seems to work is to explain why you believe what you believe each time you express an opinion.

Evidence that supports your point of view helps other people to see your point. When people state their opinions without explaining what justifies them, others are more likely to question their viewpoints. Whenever you need to convince someone of something, or when you're trying to decide between several alternatives, presenting evidence that supports a point of view is critical.

The same is true in convincing yourself that you have made a good decision. You should be able to justify a decision with evidence. Then you will be more sure of your decision and more likely to make good decisions.

When you are planning the design of a product or process, it is often useful to hear from others. They can help you see how well your design meets the criteria of the challenge. You need to present reasons for the decisions you made. Then others can help you identify misconceptions you might have. They can also help you be more confident about your decisions. They can help you judge your decisions not simply based on opinion but based on evidence and information.

An important benefit of a *Plan Briefing* is that different teams can learn from each other. A team may have struggled with one aspect of its design. That team may now have good advice for those who haven't yet tackled that problem. They, in turn, may benefit from experiences some other team has had.

PBIS

4.6 Build and Test

Build and Test Your Parachute

The moment has arrived. You have planned your best design based on evidence you have available. You have presented it to others. You have received advice from your classmates. You might have even revised your plan based on what your classmates suggested. You are now ready to build your best parachute. You hope to have the parachute that falls the slowest. If you do, it will be included in millions of cereal boxes worldwide!

Build Your Parachute

You will work with your group to create and test your final parachute. You will have the opportunity to revise it up to three times. After you have completed your third or fourth iteration, the class will hold a demonstration and competition. Each group will get to drop their parachute three times. The average of those times will be their score. Each group will also present to the class the changes they made in their parachute design since the *Plan Briefing*. They will explain why they made those changes. They will also explain what were the effects of the changes. When you recommend a parachute design to the cereal company, you'll need to tell them not only how to design the parachute but why you think that design is the best one. On the next page are some hints for you about how to manage iteration to build a better parachute.

Iteration

Iteration is a process of making something better over time. That something may be a product or an understanding. Scientists and student scientists iteratively understand new concepts better over time. Designers iteratively make designs better over time. Each time they test a design, they might find ways to improve it. Recall that each change and new design is called an iteration.

Sometimes your design does not work as well as you expected. Your first feeling may be to throw away those failed plans and begin again. Don't! If you began with a design based on evidence and science, then your parachute will probably work well with some changes.

You saw the power of iteration earlier in this unit. In the *Sandwich-Cookie Challenge*, you improved the procedure for doing the test. You performed a procedure. Then you reflected on it. You were able to find mistakes and improve your method. During the *Whirligig Challenge*, you iteratively improved your explanations. Now, with your parachute, you will have the opportunity to *iteratively* enhance a design.

There is an important thing to remember as you iterate on your design. Do not make too many changes in a design. Otherwise you will not be able to identify why the new design worked differently. Usually the best way to iterate is to make one revision at a time. Make and test one change at a time. Then you will know the effect of that change.

Test Your Parachute

Below are some suggestions for testing your designs. You can also use a page similar to the one shown to record your work.

Testing Your Designs

In experiments, it is important to run several trials. Then you can be sure your results are consistent. The same is true in testing a design. Each time you test a design, make sure to drop it enough times. Choose the number of times that will allow you to see how it performs. Be sure, too, to follow the same procedure each time you test it. Otherwise, you will not know if the design is causing the effects you see or if something you did not control in your procedure is responsible for your results.

Recording Your Work

As you test and revise your design, it will be important to record the results of your tests. You will also need to record the changes you are making. You should record why you are making those changes. This is for several reasons:

- Sometimes, what seems like a mistaken approach turns out to work better when some other part of the design is changed.

- You may need to remember what you did and did not test.

- You can use your earlier designs to help teach others.

- Study your earlier designs. You can learn how your mistakes and successes contributed to your science understanding.

You can save time by copying the working parts of a design directly. You do not have to rewrite them each time.

You will use *Testing My Design* pages similar to the one shown to record your results, changes, and the reasons for changes. Use one page for each iteraton.

Testing My Design

Name:_____ Date:_____

Each time you build and test a design idea or model, you need to test it in a fair way and record the results of that test. Use this sheet to help record your various design ideas and the result of each design.

Draw a simple sketch of your design idea or model. The sketch should help others clearly understand what the design /model looks like.	What is the key idea you were testing in this design or model?
	What did you learn from this model? Explain how effective this design or model is at accomplishing the challenge or solving the problem.
What happened when you tested the design or model?	What change do you want to test next?

Communicate Your Design

Solution Briefing

While you are working on iterating towards a better design, your teacher might have you present your design-in-progress to the class in a short *Solution Briefing*. Recall that a *Solution Briefing* is very much like a *Plan Briefing*. However, it is important for it to move faster and have more focus. If your teacher calls a *Solution Briefing*, be prepared to briefly present your progress. Hold up the design you are working on. Tell the class how it is different from what you thought you were going to build. Explain why it is different. Tell them anything you are having trouble with, and ask for advice. Your group's experience may provide valuable lessons for others. If you are having trouble, a *Solution Briefing* will give you chance to get help.

Remember, you can learn a lot from attempts that did not work as well as you expected. Do not be shy about presenting what has not worked as well as you expected. You and others can learn from mistakes. Your peers can give you advice about design, construction, and testing.

Solution Showcase

After every group has a chance to iterate several times on their designs, it will be time to finish this activity. You will present your final design in a *Solution Showcase*. Recall that a *Solution Briefing* is a presentation that allows presenters and audiences to communicate effectively about a design or product. This time, however, you will not get a chance to make your parachute design better. However, after the *Solution Showcase* you might find that these presentations help you understand the science you are learning.

Explain why you think you might have a very slowly falling design.

Introducing a *Solution Showcase*

The goal of a *Solution Showcase* is to have everyone better understand how each group approached the challenge. You get the opportunity to see the variety of solutions that might work. You can also learn what both successful and unsuccessful designs reveal about the way the world works. Be sure to discuss how you included the *Explanations* and *Recommendations* that the class generated in your final design.

A *Solution Showcase* should include the history of your design. Review your original design plan. Then tell the class what happened when you tested it. Talk about how you explained those results. Then report what you did to revise your design. Make sure to present the reasons you made the changes you did. Do this for the whole set of iterations you did. Make sure that the class understands what your final design is. Your teacher will tell you how long you have to present. You will not have a lot of time. Figure out how to present your design's history quickly.

As you listen, it will be important to look at each design carefully. You should ask questions about how the design meets the criteria of the challenge. Be prepared to ask (and answer) questions such as these:

- What techniques were tried and how were they done?
- How well does the design meet the goals of the challenge?
- How did the challenge constraints affect the use or success of this design?
- What problems remain?

Test Your Final Design

After the *Solution Showcase*, it will be time to find out which parachute falls the slowest. Each group will drop their parachute three times. Your class or teacher will decide on a procedure. Different people use stopwatches differently. It will be important to have a procedure that measures time of fall consistently. You will probably find that one or two parachutes perform a lot better than the others. Identify the best parachutes. Discuss with the class why these parachutes performed so well. Think about how each one was designed using the concepts of gravity and air resistance.

Update the *Project Board*

After you have completed your Parachute Challenge, your teacher will take you back to your Project Board for one final edit. You will focus mainly on the middle and last column, filling in what you have learned about how things fall.

Decide as a class what you should tell the cereal company. Your teacher may ask you to write a letter with recommendations to the president of the company.

What's the Point?

In design, iteration is an important part of the process. The best products are never from the first draft of the design. They are usually the result of several iterations. Early designs are important. They help designers to see weaknesses in the product. They help them to refine criteria. They also give them a chance to specify constraints more carefully. Designers are then able to figure out how to make the product and what materials to use. The result can be a product that is cheaper to produce or that meets users' needs better than the original design. The best products have a history of much iteration.

4.7 Address the Challenge

Advise the Cereal Company

Your challenge was to advise the cereal company about the design of a parachute for inside their cereal boxes. The parachute needs to be inexpensive and easy to put together, and it needs to fall slowly. After updating the *Project Board*, you will decide what advice to give the cereal company and write a letter to the president.

Update the *Project Board*

Now that you have completed the *Parachute Challenge* and discussed why the slowest parachutes in the class fell so slowly, it is time to go back to the *Project Board* for one final edit. You will focus mainly on the middle and last columns, filling in what you have learned about how things fall and identifying how what you've learned applies to designing a slowly falling parachute. Add recommendations to the last column based on your discussions about what made the slowly falling parachutes so slow to fall.

Address the Challenge

Decide as a class what you should tell the cereal company. Then write a letter to the cereal company president letting him know what kind of parachute to include in cereal boxes. Remember that good advice includes recommendations that are supported with evidence and science knowledge. Your reasoning will be very important to the cereal company.

Address the Big Challenge

How Do Scientists Work Together to Solve Problems?

You began this unit with the question: *How do scientists work together to solve problems?* You did several small challenges. As you worked on those challenges you learned about how scientists solve problems. You will now watch a video about real-life designers. You will see what the people in the video are doing that is like what you have been doing. Then you will think about all the different things you have been doing during this unit. Lastly, you will write about what you have learned about doing science and being a scientist.

Watch

IDEO Video

The video you will watch follows a group of designers at IDEO. IDEO is an innovation and design firm. In the video, they face the challenge of designing and building a new kind of shopping cart. These designers are doing many of the same things that you did. They also use other practices that you did not use. As you watch the video, record the interesting things you see.

After watching the video, answer the questions on the next page. You might want to look at them before you watch the video. Answering these questions should help you answer the big question of this unit: *How do scientists work together to solve problems?*

Left: *A trio of designers reviews a proposed concept framework together.* **Middle:** *A project team compares a series of models for a skate park layout.* **Right:** *The informal atmosphere of a lounge area acts as a backdrop to a group brainstorm.*

Stop and Think

1. List the criteria and constraints that the design team agreed upon. Which criteria and constraints did the team meet? In your opinion, what other criteria and constraints were not included in the team's discussion?

2. Why did the team split into smaller groups? What did the team hope to accomplish by doing this?

3. What types of investigations did you see the teams doing? What information were the teams trying to collect? Discuss how the information they collected helped the team design a better shopping cart.

4. Why do you think team members' ideas were not being criticized during the initial stages of design?

5. Give at least three examples from the video of how this group of people kept themselves on track to reach their goal on time. (How did they keep the project moving along?)

6. Analyze the team's final product. List three advantages and three disadvantages that you see in the new shopping cart.

7. Compare the practices you saw in the video to the practices that you used in the classroom. How are they different? How are they the same?

8. Give examples from the video of collaboration and design practices that you did not use in the classroom.

9. List two aspects of the IDEO work environment that you liked. List two aspects you didn't like.

10. There are additional responsibilities the IDEO workers have to take on in order to maintain their fun, yet productive, work environment. Identify and discuss at least three of these responsibilities.

11. Relate the responsibilities you have identified to working with a group in the classroom. Justify your choices using evidence.

Reflect

The following questions review the concepts you have learned in this unit. Your goal was to understand how scientists solve problems. You should start thinking about yourself as a student scientist. The things you are learning about how scientists solve problems will help you solve problems in the classroom and outside of school too.

Write a brief answer to each question. Use examples from class to justify your answers. Be prepared to discuss your answers in class.

1. *Teamwork* – Scientists and designers often work in teams. Think about your teamwork. Record the ways you helped your team. What things made working together difficult? What did you learn about working as a team?

2. *Learning from other groups* – What did you learn from other groups? What did you help other groups learn? What does it take to learn from another group or help another group learn? How can you make *Plan* and *Solution Briefings* work better?

3. *Informed decision-making* – What is an informed decision? What kinds of informed decisions have you had to make recently? What do you know now about making informed decisions that you didn't know before this unit? What role do experimental results play in making informed decisions? Provide an example of using experimental results from this unit.

4. *Iteration* – If at first you don't succeed, try, try again. But simply trying again isn't enough. What else do you need to do to be successful? What happens if your design doesn't work well enough the second time?

5. *Achieving criteria* – What's a criterion? How do you know which criteria are important? What if you can't achieve all of them? How did you generate criteria? On which challenges were you able to achieve the whole set of criteria? How did you have to decide which ones to achieve?

6. *Running experiments* – What does it mean to do a fair test? What's hard about doing a fair test? What did you learn about running experiments successfully that you didn't know before? Use examples from class to illustrate your answer.

7. *Controlling variables* – What does it mean to control variables? What happens if you don't control important variables? Some variables are more important to control than others. Why? Use examples from class to illustrate.

8. *Using cases to reason* – Scientists and engineers build on each other's work. Sometimes they build on the completed work. Sometimes they build on the ideas of others. You did that as well. What are the benefits of using the ideas and solutions of others? What does it take to understand what other students in your class present?

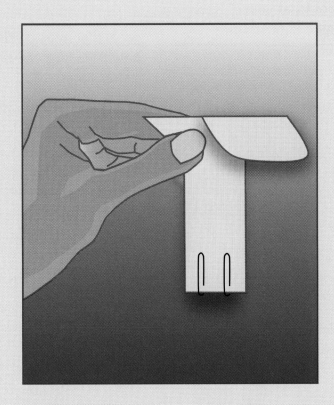

Glossary

air resistance (drag)
the opposing push that resists the movement of an object through air.

atom
a small particle of matter.

center of mass
an imaginary point on or near an object around which the object's matter is equally distributed.

claim
a statement of what you understand or a conclusion that you have reached from an investigation or set of investigations.

collaborate
to work together.

compression
reducing size by squeezing.

constraints
factors that limit how you can solve a problem.

control variables
in an experiment, the variables that are kept constant (not changed).

criteria
goals that must be satisfied to be able to successfully achieve a challenge.

dependent (responding) variables
in an experiment, the variables whose values are measured. Scientists measure how these variables respond to changes they make in a manipulated variable.

distribution
spread.

evidence
data collected during investigations and trends in that data.

fair test
things that are being compared are being tested under the same conditions and the test matches the question being asked.

folding
reducing length by bending over.

force
a push or pull on an object.

gravity
a pull between two objects.

independent (manipulated) variable
in an experiment, the variable that the scientist intentionally changes.

Investigation Expo
a presentation of the procedure, results, and interpretations of results of an investigation.

interpret
to find the meaning of something.

iteration
a repetition that attempts to improve on a process or product.

line plot
a display of data in which each data item is shown as an "x" above its value on a number line.

load
the amount of push or pull a structure has to resist.

manipulated variable
see independent variable.

matter
anything that has mass and takes up space.

mechanism
the way the parts of an item connect and move.

Messing About
an exploratory activity that gives you a chance to become familiar with the materials you will be using or the function of the project you will be designing.

molecule
the combination of two or more atoms.

phenomenon
something that happens. The plural of phenomenon is phenomena. (The word comes from Latin.)

precision
how close together the measured values are.

Project Board
a space for the class to keep track of progress while working on a project.

range
the zone between the largest and smallest solution results.

Glossary

reason
a statement that connects the claim to the evidence and science in a logical way.

recommendation
a claim that suggests what to do in certain situations.

repeatable
when someone follows the reported procedure, they get similar results.

replicate
to run a procedure again and get the same result.

responding variable
see dependent variable.

science knowledge
knowledge about how things work gathered from reading or research, or discussion that helps you understand why a claim is true.

Solution Briefing
an opportunity during the design process to share design plans and obtain advice from others.

stable
able to resist tipping over.

strong
able to withstand force.

strong structures
structures that resist folding and compressing.

structure
the way the parts of an item are put together.

template
a pattern.

trend
a pattern or a tendency.

trial
one time through a procedure.

variable
a quantity whose value may change (vary) over the course of an experiment.

variation
a wide spread of data.

volume
the amount of space that something takes up.

Picture Credits

Photos on pages 4, 16, 17, 18, 72: *Jason Harris.*

Photo on page 11: *IDEO, Robert Carra, 2001.*

Photos on page 100: *IDEO, Nicholas Zurcher.*

Photo on page 31: *Amy Scoop.*

Photos on pages 35, 42: *Mekea Z. Hurwitz.*

Photos on pages 13, 15, 19, 29, 42, 44,
65, 70, 74, 75, 82, 87, 88: *iStockphoto.*

Photos on pages 25, 57, 59, 67, 98: *Fotolia.*

All illustrations: *Dennis Falcon.*

All technical art: *Marie Killoran.*